Lady on a Donkey

Lady on a Donkey

by BETH PRIM HOWELL

E. P. Dutton & Company, Inc.
New York, 1960

To My Mother, BETTY PRIM
who has been asking me why
I didn't write a book since
the day I was born

Acknowledgments

YOU COULD say that a book is written in great part by all the people the author has ever known. Certainly some of the thoughts of those people become a part of the author's thinking. That is the case here.

Some mighty wonderful people have become a part of my thinking, to provide encouragement, stimulation, wisdom, spiritual understanding—just when these were needed most. My parents, my teachers, my friends, my editors, strangers who tossed me a thought in passing, even my enemies (who are really friends in disguise), have willed me a living inheritance. Indeed, I feel I must be the world's richest receiver.

This book, written chiefly in the prelude hours of the day, is my small effort to lower my indebtedness, spiritually and mentally, to the world and the people in it. I have found the people I have known very wonderful and helpful. No wonder the Lord loves them.

Particularly loved and remembered by the author are: Professor Ben L. Morrison who gave me a "C" minus in the only journalism course I took in college because I worked at writing only when inspiration struck (and it almost never struck), then let me write a full-length column on the editorial page of his newspaper each week because he thought I had "something," though I'm sure he couldn't imagine just what; Professor M. B. Molloy who taught us English, and then some, at the same college—East Central State, in Ada, Oklahoma; the late Dr. A. Linschied, the president, who took the time to tell me—an all-knowing sophomore—that to be a real writer one has to have something to say; Professor Foster-Harris of the University of Oklahoma, and Jill, his wife perfect, who tried to inspire me to write—the former by pointing out techniques of the craft, the latter by feeding me fried chicken.

And Mr. Fred Tarman, owner of the Norman *Transcript*, who hired me as his sole sports writer to cover the University of Okla-

6

homa, when I didn't know the difference between a touchdown and a touchback, and I remember that he was a kind, understanding boss. And Harold Keith, sports publicity director at O. U., who explained football to me.

Also, Dr. C. Dan Proctor, former president of Oklahoma College for Women at Chickasha, Oklahoma, who told me when I was very small that I was a "poet with words" and I didn't really want to be a lady detective, did I? And Mr. and Mrs. E. K. Gaylord, publishers of the *Oklahoman and Times*, Oklahoma City; Mr. Ralph Sewell, city editor; Mr. Carl K. Stuart, former managing editor; the late Harold Johnson, Sunday magazine editor; Miss Edith Johnson, columnist; Mrs. Edith Copeland, Book Editor; and Charles Bennett, managing editor—all of the same editorial staff.

I should also add Dr. Charles L. Allen, pastor of Grace Methodist Church in Atlanta, Georgia; Dr. Harry Denman, head of evangelism in the Methodist Church; Dr. Joe Burton, editor of *Home Life Magazine*; Dr. Porter Routh, executive secretary of the Executive Committee of the Southern Baptist Sunday School Board; the late Dr. C. C. Morris, Ada, Oklahoma; Dr. William H. Wallace, Jr., former pastor of St. Luke's Methodist Church, Oklahoma City; Dr. C. Ralston Smith, pastor of First Presbyterian Church, Oklahoma City; the Rev. J. Clyde Wheeler, pastor of Crown Heights Christian Church, Oklahoma City; Mrs. E. R. Reno, executive secretary of the Oklahoma City Council of Churches; all my friends at Wesley Methodist Church, Oklahoma City; Second Church of Christ, Scientist, Oklahoma City; Rabbi Israel Chodos, Rabbi of Temple Sinai in Los Angeles; and the Rev. R. T. Williams, vice-president, Pasadena Nazarene College in California.

Specifically, I want to thank Mr. Mustafa El Rafii, brilliant young Egyptian graduate student at the University of Oklahoma, for going over the first rough-draft manuscript for accuracy. His kind helpfulness was of great value.

Also, my deep appreciation to Dr. Daniel A. Poling in New York who once encouraged me to take up serious writing long before I met the "Lady on a Donkey"; and to my friends in the Penwomen of Oklahoma City, and in the High Noon Toastmistress Club.

And to all those at the Assemblies of God headquarters in Springfield, Missouri, who have cooperated with me and encouraged me in innumerable ways—the Philip Crouches (who spent

8

several years with Miss Trasher in Egypt), Carl Conner, Mrs. Christine Carmichael, and all the others—I am forever grateful.

To my husband, Carl, and Missy, my six-year-old daughter, for patience and understanding beyond the call of husbands and six-year-olds.

And to my mother who has inspired me always. How much can a mother inspire a daughter? There's no limit to measure!

And to Mama Lillian Trasher, godmother of Egypt, about whom this book was written. What kind of love and appreciation could I express in mere words? To me she is a John Wesley, a St. Francis of Assisi, an Albert Schweitzer—and I am so happy that at last the world will know her tremendous story through this book.

Finally, gratitude to my dear friend, Miss Mary Agnes Thompson, who, while living, inspired and encouraged me in so many ways I couldn't begin to relate them, and in dying, gave me new incentive to live, and write *Lady on a Donkey*.

Illustrations

Lady on a Donkey

Chapter I

LILLIAN TRASHER turned her sleeping face full to Egypt's mysterious moonlight on the Nile, then smiled at what she saw in a secret dream. In an instant she was far from Egypt and ten years old again back in the little deep-South coastal town of Brunswick, Georgia, in America. Now she was riding good old Daisy bareback across the fields to Jerdy's house. The old horse slowed to an easy trot and Jerdy, her bosom pal, made a fast leap and slid on behind her. "Let's go swimmin'," they yelled as one, the way they thought. A quick cloud of dust and the two girls were off for the river. A short hour later, refreshed and eager for further action, they boarded old Daisy again. "Let's hunt nuts," Lily yelled. "Yeee-eee—ho!" Jerdy responded shrilly, and bouncing jubilantly up and down with Daisy's lumbering gait, they headed for a secret grove of trees at the edge of town.

Christmas of that year Lily would never forget. The low marshy countryside was running over with good piney smells and so pretty it needed painting. It was 1896, the big war with the North was heard about only occasionally in evening front porch talk, like a bad dream from a grim past, and peaceful little Brunswick, never much disturbed by outside events, was settled once again within itself. Lily's family had come there from Boston, that northeastern territory known by the whites in this far southeast corner of Georgia as "Lincolndom" a generation ago, and though newcomers of only five or ten years standing were generally considered tourists and strangers, the bright-eyed little girl and her older sister, Jennie, were welcomed by Southern townsfolk without reservations.

Lily loved the carefree, exuberant life she found in this lovely village. It didn't bother her that her Quaker family had lived bountifully in a fine home in Boston and had as a close family friend the famed pulpiteer, Henry Ward Beecher, and that now in Brunswick, Georgia, they lived frugally in a tiny cottage by a canal. She didn't understand or question the reasons, but she liked the change to the simple living she now knew. Vaguely she recalled her mother telling that she had been graduated from a college called Vassar before her marriage and had traveled in Europe to complete her education. There had always been plenty of money—until now. But money, or the lack of it, was of no consequence to Lily who much preferred bouncing along on old Daisy's back in the open fields to living a cultured, sheltered life in Boston. One thing she never forgot, in Boston, Brunswick, and back in Jacksonville, Florida, where she was born: family worship in the evenings. She never did understand the prayers; they always seemed too deep for her. But those evenings together—they never left her.

Late in the afternoon that Christmas in 1896, Jerdy's parents, Ed and Anna Mason, knocked on the door of the Trasher cottage on the banks of the old Brunswick canal. It was an exciting day, one of those tingling cold-warm days in the deep South's midwinter. The two little girls had run through the piney woods gathering pine knots for

the fireplace. The fire made, they relaxed before its warmth
as the older folks talked about spring plowing for cotton,
the long rainy spell and always, hard, hard, hard times.
"Sometimes I think we oughta raise wheat th' way they
say," Ed said bleakly. "Then agin, I dunno. They's a lot
to be done with rice and cotton. I hate to think of changin'.
. . . Yep, hate to think of changin'. . . ."

He pushed his cane-bottomed chair closer to the wall,
leaned back, and stared into the fire. "It's been a long time
since we've tasted any wheat bread," he said finally. "Jes
cain't git no wheat. And th' price of cotton is clair down
to four cents a pound. These times sure is hard on folks
that's always raised cotton. Dunno what we'd do without
the Lord." Ed lowered his deep bass voice even more,
heaved his big body forward and brought his chair down
foursquare on the board floor with a thud. He leaned
toward the others and began to talk quietly, so quietly Lily
could scarcely hear him. Finally, she became so curious that
she left the other children playing in the corner and pulled
a wooden stool close beside Ed Mason. With slow, sure
voice Anna's husband was telling how he once had been a
wicked sinner. One day, he said in a steady low tone, he
had come across a camp meeting in a nearby town.

". . . and the Lord saved me."

Lily turned in the silence and stared at the faces of the
people in the firelight. They were alert, intent, all focused
on Ed and his words. Those wonderful words. Only the
sparking, zinging, hissing of the piney fire made any sound
or light. Those words! Those strange, wonderful words. . . .

Those words filled Lily's mind with wonder and awe.
She kept listening. Ed was smiling big and looked happier

than she had ever seen him. All the weary, sad notes were gone from his voice when those magic words about his Lord came out.

Later, as the Masons left, Anna Mason called back: "We're going to have a prayer meeting at our house Wednesday night. Whyn't you folks come on over?"

Lily did better than that. She ran all the way across the fields to see Anna early the next morning. She loved Anna Mason and the big happy family around her.

This Monday morning there was a great fire under the old iron washpot in the yard. It was washday at the Mason house—that magical, wonderful time with coffee perking and bacon frying on the big black stove in the kitchen and clean hot steam floating skyward from the old black washpot under the trees. This morning was sunny, clean-smelling, and though it was Christmastime the morning air was warm enough to wash in the open. And there was a promise in the sky of warmer air to come. Anna was punching her clothes with a sawed-off broomstick. The fresh, pungent smell of homemade lye soap boiling the white clothes in the big old iron pot symbolized a special kind of clean order and rhythm to Lily. Above them a mockingbird sang cheerily. On the ground a hungry robin came close to hunt for his worm breakfast. Lily stopped abruptly. Every fiber of her earnest young being wanted to sketch and paint the beauty before her and around her. Almost she could see it on paper now. Only trouble was, she was always doing things. Lots of things. She saw the sunshine filter through the massive moss-draped live oak trees, rove around on Anna's back as she leaned over the washboard. Then, off flashed the sunlight as if sprayed by a thousand mischievous little breezes into the quiet, lazy, peaceful shade. It was truly a wonderful picture, at the same time tranquil and full of movement. Meanwhile the little girl's mind whipped around through a patch of thorny questions. She balanced herself on an upturned bucket near the washpot, waited while Anna came out of the kitchen.

"Anna," she said, coming right to the point as was her usual practice, "I came over to ask you what your husband was talking about last night."

Anna straightened herself, brushed a strand of moist hair from her eyes. "Lily, child," she said, "there ain't nothing much I kin tell you. He jes got saved and it changed all his mean ways." A pretty, soft light illuminated Anna's blue eyes then as she looked into the little girl's eyes a minute. Then she sighed and began the rhythmical rub-uh-rub-uh-rub-uh-rub-uh-rub-uh—

"Anna—I—I'll help you do all your washing," Lily burst out, "if you'll talk about it while we wash."

The young woman shook her head resignedly, then smiled broadly at her friend. "All right, honey. If that's what you want." Lily tumbled the upturned water bucket behind her in her haste, quickly righted it, and ran to the washboard. She picked up a grimy workshirt and began scrubbing at such a furious rate that the whole meter of the tranquil moving picture threatened a violent upset.

Anna measured out the bluing into the last tub thoughtfully, calmly, steadily, in sharp contrast to her young friend's actions, then began to speak in a soft faraway voice. The fire under the old black washpot had been started at sunup before Ed left for the fields. Lily knew from experience how long was Anna's washday. She knew too that the tedious job would take hours more. For Anna's family was large, and every particle of dirt in the clothing and linens had to be scrubbed minutely no matter how much the back ached, or how long the job stretched ahead. The white things had to go into the boiling pot. And the light-colored clothes had to be scalded. Then a rinse and a second scrubbing—lightly this time, but thorough, nonetheless. Then rinsed again, blued, and finally hung on the wire fence to dry.

Now Anna hesitated. Lily knew she was measuring her words as well as she had measured the bluing, so important were those words. Somehow Lily knew her friend's words would be just right, like the amount of bluing she put in the clothes. The words would be perfect and pure and white, like the clothes when Anna was through with them. Anna spoke firmly, softly:

"I don't know how to say it except—except the Lord loves you—the way He loves Ed and me and everyone else in the world. And He needs you and you need Him."

Prayer meeting Wednesday night began shortly after dark when the supper dishes were washed and the kitchen swept. Lily and Jerdy had dried the dishes and put them up so fast that Anna laughed and said that they ought to have a prayer meeting every night if the girls were so affected. They sat down around the crackling fire in the old stone fireplace with the neighbors and after a while everybody grew very quiet. In the stillness Ed Mason's big voice rumbled into a song Lily had never heard before. Soon everyone was joining in heartily:

Let us labor for the Master from the dawn 'til
setting sun;
Let us think of all His wond'rous love and care.
And when all our life is over, and our work on
earth is done
When the roll is called up yonder, I'll be there.

Ed swung open his long arms, looked toward the rafters
and launched into the chorus with slow, pulsating rhythm:

When the r-r-r-r-r—o—o—ll is called up yon—der
When the r-r-r-r-r—o—o—ll is called up yon—der
When the r-r-r-r-r—o—o—ll is called up yon—der
When the r-r-r-r-r—o—o—ll is called up yon—der
I'll be there.

"Amen," said Anna sitting close by Lily. Her face looked
positively heavenly, Lily thought. She would be there when
her roll was called. Ed would, too.

"Where does that leave me?" Lily looked at Jerdy feeling
very much concerned about herself and her friend.

Now Ed was leading out on one they all seemed to know
—except Lily.

Amazing grace, how sweet the sound
That saved a wretch like me—

"Wretch!" Lily churned the thought through her mind
shook her head. Anna's sweet high voice was clear and
sure, with the others:

For once I was lost, but now I'm found
Was blind, but now I see.

Then Ed was kneeling, and gradually they all got to their knees. The two little girls knelt chiefly because they didn't know what else to do. But Lily regretted it because the rough-hewn floor was hard and splintery and the prayers went on for nearly an hour. Finally Ed closed with a benediction and Lily eyed the prayer part of prayer meeting warily as she pulled herself up. From the look on Jerdy's face, she seemed to be having the same feelings. This was far more confining than riding old Daisy bareback across the fields or swimming in the river. The grownups sat down, Ed cleared his throat. Then he opened his Bible and began to read, slowly because he wasn't a good reader, but with great feeling because he was so in earnest.

"For God so loved the wur-rld— He did—that He gave His only begotten Son that whosoever believeth on Him should not perish, but have everlasting life."

He hesitated, uncertain with words, then went on to tell again how he had been a wicked sinner, that he had come across a camp meeting in a nearby town and was saved. He didn't preach long, but somehow Lily began to listen. She was still listening and searching when Ed stopped and closed with a prayer.

Some people might have said Ed hadn't preached any sermon at all. But the words settled deep within Lily. As she left she heard a deep voice behind her: "I'm going to call on you to pray at the next prayer meeting, Lily." She turned and found Ed Mason smiling at her.

"Me—pray?"

"You could try, child."

Lily tried hard to look unconcerned and calm. But inside she was very excited. With her customary exuberance she shot home like a cannon ball. That night she lay awake for hours thinking up prayers. After school the next day she climbed to the barn loft at home with paper and pencil and pondered a long time. "Oh Lord. . . . Oh Lord, our great Benefactor and Observer. . . ." She continued to write long and impressive words. She heard her older sister, Jennie, calling her to supper, but Lily found it more convenient not to hear. And she kept working with the long words with which she wanted to impress the Lord, not to mention the folks who would be at prayer meeting the next Wednesday night. Finally it was memorized. She said the words to the hens nesting on the far side of the barn. They blinked sleepily, fussed mildly at the disturbance.

When Ed called on her to pray the following Wednesday night, she should have done very well. But she didn't. The "Great Observer" and the "Great Benefactor" had left her. Finally, she gasped in desperation. And in real prayer, she uttered a real prayer, though it didn't seem so at the time.

"Oh Lord!" she gasped in humiliation. She saw the astonished looks on the faces around her, closed her eyes and sank to her chair. Ed stood, closed his eyes and began to rumble a long, heartfelt prayer to fill the hollow space she had left.

Something strange had happened to her, however. Her whole being was filled with wonder at the experience. One sunny February afternoon in 1897, coming home from school alone, her thoughts suddenly matured. She came to an old log lying across the wooded path. There was no one here to impress. She had no thought, no need, for impressive words. Clasping her hands to her chin, using the old log for an altar, she fell to her knees. Shutting her eyes tightly, she felt a mighty presence there besides herself.

"Lord," she cried aloud, "I want to be your little girl."

The piney woods were silent, reverent. Even the birds were quiet this moment.

She prayed a long time, then was quiet, somehow completely at peace with herself. Another thought came to her, typical of her inherent do-something-about-it personality.

"Lord," she said boldly, "if ever I can do anything for You, just let me know and—and—I'll do it!"

She bowed her head. A long moment passed before she realized fully what she had done.

Silence surrounded the promise like a sudden enveloping fog. She felt a little scared, then terribly happy. She knew she meant her offer with all her being. But thinking about it was rather frightening.

How frightened she might have been if she could have seen her promise fulfilled!

Dark nights, cold nights, lonely nights in mysterious, faraway Egypt, sometimes sleeping in the village jail with her donkey because there was no other place for them to sleep; burning days on the desert, riding, riding, riding her faithful donkey, as she sought beans, rice, sugar, flour—anything for her great multitudes of orphans and widows; walking, walking, walking, leading her donkey as he carried the supplies she had gathered in the villages, in a desert heat so intense that her hair would be singed and her face burned as she trudged in home. The night her neighbor saved her from bandits. And the hours of terror with her hundred babies and children as they crouched in the old brick kiln to escape the gunfire, knives, and clubs outside.

And the night a lusty stranger followed her to the flat roof of her orphanage. . . . Could all this possibly have started with her young promise by a fallen log?

The Wesleyan Methodist minister of Brunswick who had befriended her when she told him her story baptized her a short time later in the canal near the family's cottage. She was immersed because Ed Mason had said that was the way to be baptized. She was eleven then. And she started a Sunday school for children in an old vacant house near the Wesleyan Methodist church in the village—Anna Mason's children and anyone else she could get to come around the little town. A year passed.

Now she was an inquiring twelve. An eager, awkward, galloping thirteen. A maturing, mellowing, searching fourteen. How the impatient years hurried on!

Chapter II

LILY SET her suitcase on the check counter of the old box railroad station in Asheville, North Carolina. The bag checked, she looked into the grimy long mirror in the ladies' room. She looked more than her seventeen years, she decided. Built tall and on the slender side, her long full skirts and pure white blouse all dainty with lace and gathers gave her a feeling of demure dignity she had never had riding on old Daisy or swimming in the river with Jerdy. Too, her mother had agreed she could put up her long brown hair, so now it framed the blue eyes and the girlish face with satisfying results. Very satisfying! Funny she had never noticed her looks before. She smoothed the high natural eyebrows and studied her face in the mirror. Her looks had seemed totally unimportant. More important—most important—was riding old Daisy across the fields bareback with Jerdy and swimming in the cool Brunswick River waters and helping Anna Mason wash—and listening to Anna talk about her Lord, hers and Ed's. Now, as a result of her gay, exuberant outdoor life, she supposed, her cheeks and lips were a healthy pink, her wide-set eyes were clear and seemed to be lighted with inner fires.

She turned her face slightly. She had never really noticed her features; her slender acquiline nose, her high smooth forehead. Her mother often remarked on her strong, determined jaw, but there was a softness to her face as well

24

as a look of untapped strength. Lillian walked away from the mirror, amazed, and feeling that she had just met herself for the first time.

Now she went back into the musty, dark waiting room. How smelly it was! She thought of Jennie, her older sister. How she would have shunned this dirty, musty place. Her sister, she knew, simply could not abide dirt around her. But Jennie was a stenographer now and lived in a pretty, clean, new cottage of her own in Long Beach, California. Something inside Lily longed for the same. When would she have her own home, she wondered, walking through the waiting room? Outside, the sun shone brightly, but inside the light was dull and dim. Out of the crowd, Lily suddenly made out a tiny, prim little woman dressed all in black. She seemed, in spite of her dress, a gay, alert person and Lily felt unaccountably drawn toward her. Not one to hesitate, she walked up to the woman, smiled, and said cheerfully: "It's hard to wait, isn't it, when there is so much to do?" The little woman jerked her head sharply toward Lily, then seemed to jerk forth a quick smile. Lillian moved closer to her. Now the little head in front of her nodded. There was a sigh, quick and restless. It was as if she wanted to sigh long and restfully, but didn't have time.

"Yes, there *is* so much to do, isn't there?" she finally answered. She told Lillian she was Miss Marker, Miss Myrtle Marker, and she ran the Faith Orphanage and Bible School in a little mountain town nearby. Now she studied Lily quizzically. "Do you live in Asheville?" The voice was quick, sharp, and in it Lily recognized a powerful force. Yet with the sharpness there was sureness, warmth even. Lillian sat down with her now, smoothed her skirts, relaxed.

"Yes. My family came here from Brunswick, away down in the southeast tip of Georgia, beyond Savannah, about a year ago. I'm going back now to visit my friends, the Masons, there. Then I'm coming back home through Atlanta."

Miss Marker nodded. "Atlanta's a big old place. Up and coming, they say. When I was there they put in electric trolleys. And there were factories going big, coal being mined." She turned to Lillian now, seeming to reach into her memory bag for her Atlanta bundle. "Lots of churches being built. There are two churches that were there before Sherman struck Atlanta during the war." She thought a while in silence, then looked away and continued: "The Church of the Immaculate Conception and the Second Baptist Church were all that were saved in Sherman's raid. Seems the Yankee soldiers, some of them, were Catholic, and formed a guard around the Catholic Church, though they were supposed to burn it. The Baptist Church was nearby and so was saved too. Such awful destruction—" Suddenly her mood changed, as if a signal bell had sounded. Her bright eyes flashed curiously at Lily. "But what are you going to do alone in such a big city? You must have friends there."

Lily laughed and said her mother had a friend there. But that wasn't why she was going. "I'm going to have an interview with the art editor of a newspaper there. He asked me to bring some of my drawings. If he likes them, I might get a job in the art department of the Atlanta *Georgian*. That's the newspaper—"

Miss Marker's sharp little face registered extreme shock. "Oh, my dear! Would you really work on a newspaper? A young girl of your obvious quality and refinement?"

Lily smiled and nodded that she would, gladly. "But I'm a long way from being hired yet," she said. "But tell me about your orphanage. I'm quite interested." She was interested and completely intrigued, too, by this little woman in black.

"Oh," answered Miss Marker, "it isn't my orphanage. It's the Lord's."

"Oh? Of course. Who supports it?"

Miss Marker smiled. "Why, the same One who owns it, child."

Lily straightened herself, looked directly into the eyes of the woman. "But Miss Marker, somebody has to buy food and clothes and provide shelter when you have an orphanage, even though it is the Lord's."

"That's just what I mean," said the lady. "The Lord does provide—for all our needs. In some way, and through someone, He sends us everything we need. There are a hundred children, and myself. We live from day to day—on faith."

"All the time?"

"All the time." Miss Marker's eyes gazed far beyond Lily and the long silence seemed to reaffirm her convictions. "All the time. Food, clothing, shelter, medicine. God never fails. Right now I have no food for our supper tomorrow night—nor money to buy food for my hundred children." Suddenly she leaned toward Lillian and whispered earnestly: "God knows. He knows right now where our supper is coming from. You have to have faith, Lily. Lots of faith. You have to learn to take care of all those hundred children without any money in hand. You have to go to bed at night knowing you have no food and no money to buy food for the next day, yet you must have faith to get a good night's sleep so you can get up and do your work in the morning."

It was hard to grasp—this strange, complete faith. But Lily was intrigued, and over the roar of the passenger train coming into the station she felt Miss Marker's hand on her arm and heard her shout sharply in her ear: "Why don't you come to the orphanage and help me and at the same time study the Bible and continue your schoolwork?"

It was difficult to grasp the reality of the woman's offer under such conditions. Certainly she was sincere. Lily stared past her, unable to think clearly. "I'll really have to think it over—please—" It was a plea, spoken almost soundlessly against the rumble of the train. But the noise of the train was no louder than the tumult of her own thoughts. Without looking back, without answering Miss Marker yes or no, she hurried to get on the train. Settling into her seat as the train pulled out of the station, Lily felt relieved to be able to get away from such a drastic, such a revolutionary suggestion.

At Ed and Anna Mason's in Brunswick, Lily was not surprised to see that Jerdy was now softly pretty. She studied her childhood friend's eager questioning face, heard her hungry questions about riding on a train. Did she eat her lunch on the train? Did she come all by herself? A little later when she had Lily to herself on a long evening walk, she asked breathlessly: "Did you see any strange *men* on that train?"

At that, Lily laughed. "Men?" Yes, she had. No, she hadn't talked to any. But they all seemed very nice, and she would have talked to any of them if there had been a need to.

"Lily, you wouldn't!" Jerdy's face was flushed and her eyes registered shock in the worst degree.

"Oh, Jerdy! Naturally, I wouldn't do anything wrong or indecent. But men are people, too." Lillian squeezed her friend's hand, smiled: "Men and Yankees—they're all people."

Jerdy guessed this was more or less true.

"If you ask people to treat you right, by your actions as well as your words, then they generally will do just that," Lily said flatly. "Men, Yankee or otherwise, they will treat you right if you let them. That's the way with everybody. And I'm not scared to have faith in people as well as in God. If they're people, they're God's people, aren't they?"

Jerdy seemed to be quite taken aback by all these ideas Lillian was bringing out. Lily's faith in God included people. Lillian said that's the way God meant it to be. Jerdy guessed that was all right for Lily who had been about— clear up to North Carolina which was nearly up to Yankee-land about which she had heard her grandpa talk with such fear and trembling. She mentioned this to Lily now. The things she had heard in fear though, held no fear for Lily. She laughed at her friend's fears, and hugged her warmly and kissed her flushed cheeks.

"Honey, the Civil War is over, finished. Has been for ages. Now it's time to get the fear and distrust out of our hearts and minds and reach out with love and trust." Lily suddenly laughed at herself. "What am I doing—preaching a sermon?"

Abruptly, the tension was broken. "Well," sighed Jerdy,

"if you are, you're preaching a good one." Then she gave a quick yell, and pulled Lily's arm, as she had done so often when they were children. "Let's go home and eat. I'm starved."

It was the last day of her visit before Lily had time for a long quiet talk with Anna Mason. She had thought often since she had come that her older friend looked terribly tired and worn. But the soft lights in her blue eyes were there, still, and the smiling features continued to mirror her almost incredible patience and understanding of the hard, lean circumstances of her life. Lily had been for a long walk alone that afternoon. She had breathed deeply of the sweet smells of the piney earth mixed with the salty, heady aroma the nearby Atlantic Ocean sent through the little coastal town. Finally in her wanderings she had come to the old dead log still lying peacefully, unchanged, across the path that had led to the old Trasher cottage.

On an impulse she had knelt again by the old log that had been her first altar. "Lord," she prayed. "If ever I can do anything for You, won't you let me know?" Tears came to her eyes, rolled down her cheeks. "I still mean it."

The piney woods were still, as of long ago.

"Anna," she said later as they sat together at the old round oak kitchen table. "I'm searching for something, and I don't know what it is."

Anna just smiled and patted her on the arm. Neither spoke for a long time. As only the closest of friends can, they sat quietly, reminiscing, searching, reaching for a view of the tomorrows. While Ed worked in the fields, the younger children were at school and Jerdy was gone on an errand, there was time for this sort of introspection. On the old-fashioned black stove the teakettle simmered peacefully as did the beef stew Anna had put on for supper. Finally, Anna straightened and smiled, "You've a gracious plenty of all the good things. Every day I pray that you'll find what you're searching for. You will, when the time is right."

"I pray about it, too, Anna," Lily said earnestly. "I feel as if my search is almost over—then again— Anna, would you think I was awful if I said I wanted desperately to be an artist? Even do sketches for a newspaper?"

The older woman looked past Lily across the long low fields of cotton almost ready to be picked. Her look was as steady and pure as the bluing she once had measured at the tubs in the back. Lily turned, too. Their eyes met then, and once more Lily marveled at the gentleness and wisdom of Anna's words and manner. Somehow, this little farm woman who barely knew how to read and write, who lived in the desperately meager south Georgia surroundings with her farmer husband, who had no education in philosophy, religion, the arts—somehow, she had wisdom and the understanding of the most trying and complex problems. While Lily searched for the future, Anna found her future in each moment.

Hers was a faith brimming over with contentment and peace and wisdom gained from the special place she seemed to have in God's own sight. It was a special place which Anna Mason herself had sought. She was encircled by Heaven all the time. When she moved, her Heaven moved with her, because it was in her, and enveloped her like a mighty halo. And circumstances could not change Anna's private heaven. Now she got up to stir the stew. When she sat down again her earnest eyes smiled at Lily.

"Child, I can't tell you about being an artist or not. God's planted that talent in you. Now it's coming out in full bloom. I seen it comin' when you was a little girl here with me—the way you'd talk and the pretty way you'd tell things. Looked like you was bent on being a writer or artist, even then. You used to draw on the ground even. Many's the time I'd be a-washin' and see the prettiest pictures you'd drawn in the dust. Lots of times you'd tell me a story to go with the picture, remember? When my back would git so tired and ache from stooping over so long at the washboard, it rested me to watch you draw in the dirt and to listen to all those stories you'd tell. You must of made 'em all up, 'cause I never heard 'em anywheres else. Maybe that's what God is tellin' you to do. If it is, Lily, you'll know—by listenin'. If you listen to God, you'll know. And I know you'll listen."

It was truly remarkable to Lily that the bit of Heaven that encircled Anna Mason seemed to reach out and draw into that enchanted circle the person to whom she was talking. Being with Anna was like going into a warm sunny room with mirrors that rainbowed the sunlight and sitting on soft cushions and feeling a gentle hand touch your worried mind and heart and your tired shoulders. No matter where Anna was, there was Heaven, too. Over the copper washboard, punching the boiling clothes in the black pot with the sawed-off broomstick, ironing with the heavy sadirons, cooking supper, caring for her children—whatever—Anna's private Heaven was with her. And somehow the person with her became a part of her, and her Heaven, even taking some of it along.

Now Anna patted Lily's hand gently. "You'll probably

hear a loud, clear voice telling you what to do with your life, Lily. Loud as thunder, maybe. It might not be a still, small voice for you." Anna's face broke into a tiny smile. "You're—you're so alive, child. Anything wonderful could happen to you—unless, unless you let your looks get in the way."

Lily shouted with laughter. "My looks? Anna, what's my looks got to do with it?"

"Nothing. Unless you make it so." The older woman's face was serious now. "I was taken back mighty hard when you got off the train, Lily. Your pretty looks can be the death of you and you are sure what Ed calls a 'looker.' "

The earnest voice was a whisper now. She leaned close and studied Lily a moment before she went on. "You won't let your looks get in your way—yours and God's will you?"

"I promise. I don't think I'll have any trouble that way," Lily answered evenly. But hadn't she admired herself in the Asheville station mirror just a few days before? Or was she merely observing for the first time a fact she had not noticed before: that she had physical beauty beyond most other young women.

Now she gave her friend a quick hug as they heard Ed Mason's wagon coming into the front yard.

"Be in soon as I unhitch," he called in the same rumble of a voice Lily remembered so well.

"And the Lord saved me. . . ." How those memories pushed into her mind when Lily heard Ed Mason's voice. "Amazing grace, how sweet the sound—" Anna and Lily smiled at each other, each seeming to read the other's thoughts. How the songs had rung out in this big old kitchen!

The children could be heard coming down the path from school. Anna looked in the warming oven and checked the yeast bread. "It'll be ready to bake in an hour," she said. "Ed," she called to her husband coming in the door, "I need some wood in the firebox. Lily dear, you can set there at the table and make a green salad. You'll have to get the onions and radishes out of the garden. I got the lettuce picked and washed in the springhouse. I'll get it, Lily. I want us to enjoy this supper real good because it'll be the last one we'll have together with Lily for a long, long time."

Lily felt she would never leave here, in her heart, that she would surely take some of the heaven that was here with her always, wherever she went. . . .

But where was she going?

Chapter III

LILY LIKED Atlanta at first sight. Huge, bustling, and new; at the same time old and smoky and tired, living leisurely like an old Civil War colonel, but eager for more glory and grandeur and willing to work for it.

Lily was staying with a friend of her mother who had a house on Confederate Avenue. That morning she put on her best long black skirt, tailored and snugly belted, and a white middy blouse with a black tie in front. Before a full-length door mirror she carefully brushed her hair, pulled it up neatly at the back of her crown. Then she unpacked her white gloves and black hat and painstakingly put them on in front of the ancient marble-topped walnut dresser. She took a last glance at the bedroom as she picked up her folder of sketches she was taking to the newspaper downtown. She had left the room neat, as her mother had reminded her to do. The dark bedstead with its high headboard and its clean, white crocheted spread seemed to fit perfectly with the rag rug on the bare wooden floor beside the bed. So did the pretty white curtains at the long, ancient, fragile-looking windows. Lily went by the kitchen, told her hostess goodbye, then hurried up the hilly walk to the electric trolley line. The homes along the way were old and tired-looking and trimmed with intricate gingerbread fanciness. The porches were neatly scrubbed and furnished with comfortable chairs. The yards and gardens

35

held masses of beautiful flowers and shrubs, and lawns were so well-kept and green they seemed almost unreal.

Lily and the electric trolley arrived at the stop almost simultaneously. On the ride to town she thought of Jerdy and her fears of boldly stepping out into the new and different. How different two friends could be, she thought, smiling a little. She actually looked forward to meeting this Mr. Howard, the newspaper art editor, even though she was excited and realized she didn't exactly know how to approach him when the time came.

Then she found herself in the smoke-filled city room of the Atlanta *Georgian*. The rattle of typewriters, the talk and confusion (or so it seemed to her), were almost overwhelming. Then on into a side room with one glass wall where the heavily mustached art editor frowned and asked her questions. Finally he leaned back, closed his eyes, and said to come back tomorrow when he had had time to look over the drawings more carefully. He had a lot of applications for the job since the ad had run, but liked what she had shown him. Right now he had a headache, a sore throat, and a deadline. Lily was dismissed.

Relaxed and happy, she walked on down Marietta Street, then half lost herself in the maze of curving, changing streets. She wandered down as far as Rich's department store on Whitehall Street and looked at the tailored autumn dresses in the windows. There were kid gloves and blouses with big lacy sleeves. She passed them by a little reluctantly.

When she went back to the paper the following morning she was told that Mr. Howard was at home with a bad cold. A strange man sitting at the art editor's desk told her he was sure someone else had been hired on the art job anyhow.

"Someone else?" For the first time Lily's voice trembled. She had been so sure she would get the job. The man was shaking his head at the piles of copy around him. "I'll never catch up," he groaned. He cupped his head in his hands and began to study a batch of sketches nervously, chomping on a long black cigar. Lily fidgeted in her chair, apparently forgotten. Abruptly, the man looked up after a while and said, "Come back in two or three days, kid. You can get your drawings back when Howard is here. I don't know where he keeps any of that stuff." Lily hurried out, trying desperately to keep back the tears until she could get to the street.

The disappointment was almost more than she could take, but worse, she wasn't even sure she would get her precious drawings back. After all the hard work she had put on them. After all her hopes. Somehow she managed to hold her tears until she got to her sunny room on Confederate Avenue. But then she fell on the bed and sobbed a long time. Finally she went to sleep. And when she awoke she could hear Anna Mason's voice as if she had been in the same room. "You'll probably hear a loud clear voice telling you what to do with your life, Lily. Loud as thunder, maybe." Then she could see Anna's smile engulfed in that same little Heaven she carried with her.

Suddenly Lily smiled. At once she knew beyond all doubt that things were happening the way they were supposed to happen. Why cry about that? She went to the service porch and washed her face in cool water, combed her hair, and went in quietly to help fix supper. She waited several days before going back to the newspaper city room for her drawings.

She was completely happy and at peace when she entered the noisy city room this time. Mr. Howard was back at his desk now and when he saw her, he smiled, then abruptly the old frown came back to his face. He took off his glasses and pointed to her sharply and exploded: "Why didn't you come back, young woman? I wanted you for that job. Now I had to hire someone else!"

Lily winced at the fierceness of his voice. She felt sorry for him then. "But I did come back," she said calmly. "I did, and they told me you had hired someone for the job."

The man jerked off his eyeshade and threw it down in exasperation. Then he seemed to gain a small measure of control and said slowly, deliberately: "I *did* hire someone. That someone was *you!* Of all the stupid, blundering idiots! Why didn't they tell you that you were the one I wanted." He groaned then and his voice softened. "I'm sorry, young lady. Sorry for myself. And sorry for you."

Lily smiled. "Don't be sorry for me." She rose quickly and took her portfolio of drawings—"and thank you for everything." She thought she saw a peculiar, quizzical look on his frowning face as she said goodbye and hurried confidently out of the smoky room.

The truth was, she could hardly wait to get to Miss Marker's Faith Orphanage in North Carolina.

It was as if a strong wind of almost hurricane force were drawing her there. It was as if a strong wind were pushing her in great gusts away from the smoky newspaper in downtown Atlanta, up toward the Faith Orphanage in North Carolina.

Chapter IV

"IT'S A STRANGE new life for me," she wrote in her diary. ". . . I am learning all things . . . how to cut out clothes, to sew, to cook and to take care of newborn babies. How to teach and oversee large numbers of children. *And how to do without!*"

She also pointed out to her diary that she was learning to trust Someone beyond herself for her needs. "I have no money at all and my people do not send me any." But she didn't write her people for money, knowing they did not understand why she had to come here. Her shoes wore out and Miss Marker had no money to buy her another pair. Then someone sent in a box of old clothes with a pair of men's shoes. So she asked Miss Marker if she might have them.

"Men's shoes—for you?" Even Miss Marker, who was completely unaware of both dress and adornment and considered personal beauty something of a drawback, apparently could not envision Lillian in an old pair of men's shoes. "My dear," she said sorrowfully, shaking her head. "They're just not your type."

Lily knew that. "If I hadn't known it," she wrote in her diary with an ironic smile, "it would not have taken long for me to find out as I walked into the classroom to teach the orphans and saw the drawing on the board of my feet with the toes sticking out—in men's shoes."

One morning Lily awoke at daylight as was getting to be her custom since it was her job to make gruel for the early orphanage breakfast. Afterward it was her duty to scrub pots and pans. Getting up at such a time gave her a head start on her long day of chores. Now she lay back in the bed, a curious, grinding pain encircling her stomach. She bent herself into a semicircle to ease the nagging pain. Gradually a realization came to her, one that she had been feeling for weeks: She was hungry. She simply wasn't getting enough to eat here at the Faith Orphanage. Too, the long hours of heavy floor scrubbing, clothes washing, cooking, ironing, and sweeping, not to mention the teaching and studying she also did, required, for her, a greater intake of nourishing food than she was getting. She had noticed that her clothes were hanging loose on her shoulders and at her waist. In the mirror she had seen deepening shadows under her eyes. But what could she do? Now she eased her weary body up from the bed. The pain had let up momentarily. She reached for her worn little coin purse under the pillow and took out twenty cents someone had given her the day before for her personal use. At the time it seemed impossible to decide what she needed the most with the twenty cents. So she had put it away carefully. Now it was very clear: she must spend it for food, something she needed and wanted. She must begin somehow to regain her strength. She was weak, tired. She thought of Anna Mason again and those fragrant Monday wash mornings. She smelled bacon frying in the kitchen as it did each morning after the hog-killing season at the Masons. Now she breathed deeply. She closed her eyes and inhaled the tantalizing odor of bacon frying in the kitchen, the fragrant apple pies Anna baked and set on the warming oven. 'That's what I'm going to have," she whispered to herself. Suddenly tears were rolling down her cheeks. Just the thought of food was overwhelming. She closed the purse and was putting it back under the pillow when she heard Miss Marker's voice, sharp and worrying, in the hall.

The gruel wasn't on cooking for a hundred breakfasts. "Are you all right, Lillian," she said, hurrying in in quick dynamic motions. Lillian shook her head a little. "I'm just a little tired this morning, I guess, and a little slow. I'll be right out."

"You are not ill, are you?" Miss Marker's voice often seemed sharp and abrupt, but she was filled with compassion beneath the sharpness, Lillian had found. Suddenly, turning to leave, she stopped. "Wonder if you could lend me the twenty cents you had yesterday, dear? I lack just that much having enough to pay the deliveryman for the groceries."

Lily felt numb. Without any feeling one way or the other she reached for the coin purse, opened it, and gave Miss Marker the precious twenty cents.

"So nice of you to lend it to me," her voice called back. "Here you are, boy," Lillian heard her call to the delivery boy. "Here's your twenty cents!"

Lillian knew too that it *was* his twenty cents. From now on. Miss Marker, bless her poor hurried heart, would not think of it again.

With the springtime, Lillian felt herself gaining some strength. She especially loved the children at the orphanage. And she still felt eternally drawn to this holy place, this wonderful mission. Yet when Miss Marker's brother and his wife asked her to go with them on preaching trips, she went gladly. This, too, drew her. She had taught the children at the orphanage. But now she would work with adults, too.

She went gladly. These were to be some her happiest hours. She could feel it. She couldn't say why. But happiness was here and now. One evening she went with the Markers to visit and stay for supper with the Goodsons, a farm family down in the valley. They went by buggy down the steep mountain road. It was a vibrant evening, alive as a ten-year-old on a picnic. It was a merry, puckish, enchanted late spring moment of time in North Carolina. Everywhere radiance shone against radiance. The picture was breathtaking—mountainsides exploding with rich, red rhododendron bloom, mountain springs poking their bubbling heads playfully and naughtily in and out of their lopsided mountain playhouses; birds, birds, birds—singing, singing, singing—to their mates, to the squirrels, to the mountain springs, to their Maker, and even to the mortals who passed below in the old black buggy.

The buggy now followed the turn in the winding road to a broad white gate, behind which was a large neat farmhouse with a comfortable broad veranda spreading across the front. There were curving rows of young plants everywhere following the curves of the good earth which nourished them. A large red barn and outhouses sat in the rear. The road by-passed the house for the barn. Now Brother Goodson was opening the road gate for them to enter and when they had passed they stopped to wait for him. When he came alongside there was handshaking and laughter, then introductions. For with him was a tall, clean-cut, muscular young man—a minister here to help with the home mission work. Brother Goodson's voice faded for Lily when she looked down from the buggy and saw the young man's handsome gray eyes looking directly into hers. Tom Jordan. . . . Or did she only fancy she had caught his name. Was she being helped down from the buggy by his strong, firm grasp? Or was she floating? All that springtime ever was meant to be in the hearts of the young surrounded her and engulfed her now, and she sighed, "Lord, did You lead me here tonight?"

Tom smiled, tall and serious, as he walked with long easy strides.

She saw as she walked toward the porch a rainbow stretched out high in the sky, caught inextricably between a high mountaintop rain and the setting sun. How thrilling to be caught in the midst of a mountain rain and the glow of the evening sun, now gentle and slumbering in its nest of western mountains. How secure to be caught inextricably! She turned impulsively to this gray-eyed young man, smiled, and caught her breath as she realized that the gray eyes were still on her.

And she liked it.

They both laughed from sheer exultation and moved slightly toward each other. Mrs. Goodson called out supper, then. "Ah'm mighty pleased to have met you, Miss Trasher," she heard him say as they moved with the others to the supper table. She said nothing, answering him with her eyes.

The big farm table was literally overflowing with fried chicken, baked ham, poke salad, mashed potatoes and gravy, grits, string beans, hot biscuits, and homemade blackberry preserves. Young Tom Jordan asked the blessing before they ate. As he prayed Lily had an excellent chance to look

at him, though her eyes were supposed to be closed like
the others'. How different he was! How rich and mellow and
decent was his voice. Lily was twenty-two now. She guessed
he must be only slightly older than herself.

It was a delightful meal, a gracious plenty of everything,
she thought gratefully. How different from the meager,
uninteresting fare of the orphanage. Lillian felt a pang of
regret and remorse. Here she was in the midst of plenty
while her little orphanage friends had not nearly enough.
If she had been hungry all those months, hadn't they been
hungry too, with their growing young bodies? Weren't they
hungry now? Right now? How good to have more than
enough of everything one needed. But was it right to eat
so when others were hungry?

Still, how could one reach for the height and depth and
breadth to living in God's world if one were hungry? How
could you have the strength to help the hungry if you were
hungry yourself?

Across the table she was conscious of those penetrating,
handsome, gray eyes. It would seem that she and those eyes
could never be apart again now that they had found each
other. When they parted that day at the Goodsons they
both knew the parting would not be for long.

First, it was a trip to a mountain mission with the Markers. Then a country box supper at the local schoolhouse with
Tom getting Lillian's box. Then, back at the Goodson's for
dinner, seated side by side this time. Inevitably Lillian
Trasher and Tom Jordan saw more and more of each other
in the weeks that followed. Inevitably they became engaged.

That wonderful May evening of 1910 they each prayed,
together and separately. This must be God's will for each

of them. For both of them. This must be the plan that had been set up for one Lillian Trasher and another Tom Jordan eons before they were born. Lillian pondered the thought. Was this plan for another Lillian Trasher? There had been one before, she recalled.

She was riding to church in the buggy one Sunday morning with her fiancé when the strange thought came to her. She knew positively that there was a divine plan for each life. For hers. For Tom's. For everyone's life. Those who failed to find what God wanted with their lives, through lack of searching or ignorance or carelessness or willful disregard of God—these were out of tune eternally. But who was she in God's sight, anyhow? She remembered that her mother had told her of another Lillian, born a year or so before her. The first Lillian had died in infancy. And the sad mother, determined to have another Lillian as her child, had given the second baby the same name: Lillian Hunt Trasher. Sometimes now it gave her a strange feeling that she was living for someone else, that she ought to do double duty with her life. She had another thought, and it froze within her. Perhaps that other Lillian was the one intended to marry the handsome young minister so tall and confident beside her.

She had gone back to the orphanage for the summer and was busily sewing and planning for the wedding. It was only ten days now. Lillian carefully arranged her time so that everything would be in good order. She gave her bridal dress one last fitting, felt entirely satisfied with the details of the forthcoming wedding. She felt completely satisfied with her future husband. His love for her was deep—as deep as was her love for him. He was kind, thoughtful, honest—

and yes, quite handsome sitting there beside her holding the reins loosely with his strong brown hands. How capable were those hands holding the harness, working in the field, as she had seen him do. How sure they were. How fine was his active, searching mind. How she enjoyed their long, penetrating discussions about their lives and their relation to God. Now she studied his profile: strong regular features, heavy black eyebrows and strong black moustache. Strength! That was his predominant feature, she decided. Strength in faith, in God, in mind, in body, and strength in his love for her. He turned and smiled slightly with his eyes. Did she need an answer? She shook her head. No? No. Then, all was well. He turned his mind back to his sermon, apparently, his face to the road ahead. She was glad they loved each other so much that they could ride in understanding silence.

She had heard of couples, long married, who understood each other so well that they could ride for hours, each with his own thoughts, then one would suddenly complete a thought that had been discussed by them hours before. And the other would follow exactly without any break in the discussion, or any explanation needed. This seemed to be the way it was with them. She thought again of her white wedding dress. How proud she would be to wear it with Tom at her side!

Ten days before their wedding Lily and Miss Marker went to hear an address by a missionary from India. Before she had finished, Lillian was in tears. Back at the orphanage, she hurried to her room and knelt by her bed with great sobs racking her body. She stayed there a long time. Miss Marker, apparently sensing her need to be alone, stayed away until quite late. Then her knock sounded at the door.

Her voice, strangely soft, called, "Lillian, if you want me, I'll come in. If you don't, tell me and I'll leave."

Lillian pulled herself to a sitting position on the bed, wiped her eyes. "I want you to come in, please," she said.

The older woman did not sit down. "Perhaps you want to tell me what is the matter. Or perhaps you'd rather not, dear."

Her keen sensitiveness was never more apparent. Lillian deeply appreciated it now. "Nothing is wrong, Miss Marker." But then her voice broke. She said flatly, "Nothing is wrong—except I am engaged to marry the most wonderful young man in the world ten days from now—and I can't marry him."

Miss Marker frowned. "You can't marry him! Why, Lillian, he is a fine young man. And you two are so—so right for each other."

"Yes," said Lillian. "But God has called me to be a foreign missionary, and I couldn't refuse God."

Miss Marker sat down then, and pressed her hands over her eyes, obviously having trouble absorbing the shock. She looked at Lillian dully, then, and said slowly and deliberately, "You mean you've been called to be a missionary?" Lillian nodded. She couldn't think about it before, she said. Yet it was in the depths of her, all the time. Tonight she knew. She knew for sure.

"Oh, the poor, poor boy," Miss Marker said in a soft, low voice Lillian hardly recognized as belonging to the small, sharp-tongued woman she had grown to know and love so well. She shook her head sadly. "This will break his heart—"

"But I can't refuse God," Lillian said doggedly. "Can I

now? Even though I've promised to marry, I can't refuse God."

"No, Lillian. No. You must hear God first." She put an arm awkwardly around her young friend. "Where do you think you are to go?"

Lillian shook her head and said flatly, "I don't know. It's funny. I don't know where I am going, or how I am going, or when I am going. I have no sense at this point as to where to start. Yet I know I have been called and I am going. So I must start. Now."

Miss Marker smiled. For the first time since she had known the little woman, Lillian saw that her eyes were filled with tears.

"Good night, my dear. Why don't you sleep a little late in the morning." She walked briskly out of the room, apparently embarrassed at her tears, her steps resounding sharply staccato on the bare hall floors, then fading, then gone, as she closed her own door.

Lillian had but five dollars since she had spent all her money on her wedding. Characteristically she went directly to Tom to tell him what had happened. Early the next day she led him to the winding road over which they had ridden so often together. She told him everything, then they walked silently for a long time. Finally he looked at her searchingly: "Where do you think you have been called to?"

To Africa, she thought.

"I'll wait for you, Lily," he said at last. "One year— two years. Longer, my dear." He turned her to him gently, his gray eyes pleading.

"But what could I do in one or two years?" she cried

softly. "Or three or four years even." She shook her head sorrowfully. "No, Tom. This is goodbye. Now. For all time." She looked at him once more, loving him more, she thought, than she had ever loved him before. A dark veil seemed to come between them, and separate them in an instant. And they both knew their togetherness was over.

He was gone. Lillian walked slowly, alone, down the winding road to the Faith Orphanage, crying softly. How she had hurt him. . . .

Where was she going? She looked ahead, up the long, winding road that threaded through the lovely green mountains. Her future, she thought, was like the road ahead. She couldn't see where it went. But she knew it was there in front of her. To find where it went, she would have to follow it. Patiently. Faithfully. Trustingly. Calmly. Steadily.

She began to walk.

A few of her friends handed her some money for her mission travels and when she heard of a holiness missionary conference being held in Pittsburgh, Pennsylvania, she decided to go there, learn what she could, and, she hoped, discover where in Africa she was to go. Perhaps, too, He would provide a way. Lillian knew she had no church to send her. The little Buxton Street Holiness Church she attended in Asheville could not send her. They were barely able to provide for their own needs. She knew, too, that her family was not in sympathy with her plans. So she could expect no financial or moral support there. Even her closest friends were fearful. But Lillian had no doubts. No fear. God would provide a way, as he had provided for Miss Marker, her hundred orphans, and her school. Lillian, now twenty-three, began living in perfect peace with herself. It seemed almost like Anna Mason's heaven encircling her. Perhaps she now had her own private heaven around her. She smiled at the thought.

Then began a strange series of events which formed the pattern for all her future, though the incidents seemed insignificant at first.

"I handed all my money to Miss Marker for safekeeping," she wrote. "She put it in her desk, and her sister, not knowing that it was mine, used it to pay a debt.

"I didn't know of this until I was starting for the train to the missionary conference. My friends tried to help me out, but there just wasn't enough money to make up the eighteen dollars needed for train fare. However, there was enough to get as far as Washington, D.C. I had never been to that city and knew no one there.

"But Miss Marker said she had a friend there to whom she would give me a note of introduction and with whom she thought I might stay until she could send me the rest of the money for my fare to Pittsburgh.

"In due time I reached Washington, found Miss Marker's friend, and handed her the note of introduction. 'Oh, I am so sorry,' she said, 'I cannot take you in as I am entertaining a missionary family from Assiout, Egypt; but come in and have some lunch.' "

The missionaries were a Reverend and Mrs. Dunning. Lillian, their hostess explained, was a missionary to Africa.

What a lovely sound! Lillian savored the words, the idea, the anticipation that came to her when it was said. The knowledge that these words were a part of God, for her, gave her a feeling of belonging, at last, a sense of being in

the right place at the right time and heading for a pre-
arranged rendezvous with God Himself.

The missionary from Egypt was speaking now. She heard
his voice as one in the distance, she saw him as through a
glass darkly.

"Africa?" he was asking. "To what part of Africa are you
going?"

Suddenly the faces in the room became a sea of questions,
flooding toward her, engulfing her, submerging her. Somebody asked: "What board is sending you to Africa, Miss
Trasher? No board? Your church, then?"

Lillian blushed painfully. Then she calmed herself, looked
at the people in the room boldly. "I am not going out under
any board," she said flatly. "Nor is my church sending me.
In fact, at the present time, I am not even a member of a
church though I have been attending a wonderful little
Holiness Church in Asheville."

"Your family, then, I presume," said Mrs. Dunning,
smiling kindly. The Reverend Dunning moved to Lillian's
side. He was smiling, too. "Your family is sending you,
then." It was a statement, a statement of fact which he
must have reasoned was the only way left.

"Sir—" Lillian took a deep breath. "My family is not in
favor of my going at all."

Lillian would never forget the looks of sheer astonishment on the faces in the room. She saw the Reverend Dunning stop as he walked toward her, as if the shock of her
statement had frozen him in his tracks. "You mean you have
only your fare to Africa?" That a girl of her age would go
to Africa, without knowing the language and without having
any money for support, plainly seemed the height of folly

to him. Worse, a calamity for a young life. Lily, for her part, knew the man in front of her should know the conditions in Africa since he himself had been in Egypt for so long. How could she explain to him that her plans, like Miss Marker's, were built on faith, not money. She raised her head, met his eyes with a sure, level gaze. He was studying her closely now, then saying: "You mean you have only your fare to Africa?"

"Reverend Dunning, I have one dollar."

There were audible gasps in the room. Then a deathly silence. Finally she was aware of the Reverend Dunning shaking his head. Then he looked at her, frowning. "No. No. No!" he exploded. He kept staring at her, searching for a moment, then said flatly: "No!"

Later Lillian wrote in her diary: "Perhaps I'd better not try to tell you all that Brother Dunning said or thought, but I can still hear him telling me to go home to my mother."

"Faithful is He that calleth you, who also will do it," she read in her Bible that night.

One of the missionary party had given up her room at the friendly house in Washington. Miss Mattie Rast, a missionary who assisted the Dunnings in their Egyptian mission house and was sleeping in the spare bedroom, volunteered to go on to the Pittsburgh missionary conference two days early so that Lillian would have a place to stay in her room. Those two days turned out to be the most decisive in Lillian's life. The morning of the second day the Rev. Dunning called her to him and asked her to sit down. He looked at her intently, and said quietly, "Miss Trasher, my wife and I have talked it over with each other, and with God. We want you to know we believe thoroughly in your vision that you have been called to serve in a foreign field. Can you ever forgive us for disbelieving? At least, can you understand that we were all so shocked that a young girl would dare go to the other side of the world, away from all her family, away from her people, her language, her culture, without financial backing of any kind—can you understand that we simply could not comprehend such faith?"

Lillian smiled at the elderly missionary. "There isn't anything to forgive," she said. "I realize how drastic it is. But then, it has to be that way, doesn't it?" She straightened her shoulders, sighed a little tiredly. "I don't understand how I am to make this mighty step. But this one thing I know: God knows."

"Miss Trasher," the Reverend Dunning said. "I have no money to offer you—for your transportation or for salary. But would you come to Assiout, Egypt, and help us in our mission work there? We could give you your upkeep—your meals and room."

Lillian walked to the window, looked down at the hurrying pedestrians crossing the street in the rain. The heavily overcast sky was clear in the east. And there, thousands of miles east and south, lay Egypt where the Dunnings had their mission. The words penetrated Lillian's mind ever so slowly. She pondered the thought now. Wasn't she supposed to go to Africa? But wasn't Egypt a part of the continent of Africa? Of course. She closed her eyes for a long, long time. There were tears in them when she looked at the Reverend Dunning again. "I had no intention of stopping over in Washington," she said softly. "Perhaps the Lord has led me here just to meet you and Mrs. Dunning."

She closed her eyes, prayed aloud, yet to herself, as well, addressing her God only: "Lord, is this what You wanted me to do? I need an answer, Lord, so I'll know what to tell this gentleman." Then she was silent, listening carefully.

Shortly after, she opened her eyes. There were no tears in them now. "I'll go to Assiout, Egypt," she said. "Thank you very much."

The following day Lillian received her money from Miss Marker and left for the missionary conference in Pittsburgh. When she arrived she had twenty-five cents. On top of that, her trunk fell off the wagon and was badly smashed. "But the Missionary Conference people entertained the missionaries, providing them with a tent to sleep in and with table-board," she wrote, "and I was comfortable and happy."

During the conference someone else who caught Lillian's vision of service handed her eight dollars. She immediately bought a new trunk and once more packed her things to go to a foreign field—Assiout, Egypt, now.

When the conference came to a close, those around her who heard her story had given her enough money to take her to Philadelphia. From there she was to go to New York to stay until ready to sail for Egypt.

Before she left the missionary conference, however, she suffered another setback. It was one of the strange small events which shaped her future. She wrote of it in her diary: "I accompanied Mr. Dunning to the train and when he was buying his ticket, he discovered he did not have quite enough money for the long trip ahead. 'Oh, I can let you have that,' I said quickly."

She was to smile when she thought of it later, but when

the missionary's train had pulled out, and she counted the money for her fare, she was deflated considerably to find she had a transportation problem herself.

"Young lady," the clerk said kindly, "you don't have quite enough money here to buy your ticket to Philadelphia." Then, apparently sensing her distress, he added, "I'm sorry. Are you all alone?" Lillian looked at him stanchly, smiling, "I am never alone. Never!"

The railway clerk shook his head, "Nevertheless, you don't have quite enough here to pay your fare to Philadelphia." He hesitated. "Maybe I could help you out." His voice wasn't critical, but Lillian knew he had seen her give the elderly missionary some of her money. Obviously he couldn't understand how she could have been so foolish as to give her money away when she knew she was going to need it for her own fare. Now he was talking to her again. Would she accept the small amount she needed from him? A personal loan, or gift?

Lillian thanked him, but declined. "How far can I go on this money?" she asked. He checked, found she could get to Harrisburg and have a dollar left.

Suddenly she beamed. "Then give me a ticket for Harrisburg!"

Only now did she remember that a lady had given her an address in Harrisburg, and told her if circumstances ever brought her to that city she should come visit in her home.

It was night when she reached Harrisburg and it took some hunting before she found the address. They took her in, though she was not sure how glad they were to see her so soon. During her stay she was asked to speak at a mission hall, but nobody gave her any money.

When Friday came she told her hostess she was going to Philadelphia the following afternoon. Saturday at the appointed time, the gentleman of the house took her to the depot. As they approached the ticket office, he asked Lillian, "Do you have your money ready for your fare?" He smiled kindly at her. Lillian looked at her host resolutely, studying his face and wondering what his reaction would be. She couldn't help remembering her early conversations with the Reverend Dunning when he learned of her mighty dream and her empty pocketbook. Did this man guess that she had no money? She replied simply: "No, I don't have the money ready for my fare. The truth is, I don't have any money at all."

The man turned sharply, stared at her. Finally, he sighed: "You are a very remarkable young woman. Very." There was a long pause, then: "Of course, I'll be glad to buy your ticket to Philadelphia. But do you expect to get all the way to Egypt this way? On nothing?"

Lillian smiled at that. "God will see that I get to Egypt. You see, He is attending to it even now."

From Philadelphia she went to New York City arriving at the Glad Tidings Mission late on a hot and humid Saturday night in July of 1910. During her stay Lillian was invited to speak in various missions and churches. Those who heard her seemed to understand her dream and soon she had collected forty dollars. With that she went to the Thomas Cook and Son Travel Bureau. A ticket to Assiout, Egypt would be about one hundred dollars, she was told. So she paid forty dollars down to secure her berth, and wrote home telling her family she would be leaving when the ship sailed October 8th.

There was no immediate reply from her parents. Her older sister, Jennie, wrote promptly from her home in Long Beach, California, however. Jennie had used her earnings as a stenographer in that city to buy herself a little cottage. Then she had planted beautiful flower gardens and added rental cottages until she had an independent income, in addition to her salary as a stenographer. Lillian smiled when she read Jennie's letter. Her beloved older sister, who was too timid to step outside her own house in the dark, felt that she should go with her younger sister to—Lillian gasped in amazement—to *Egypt!* When she began to read the letter she thought Jennie must have been expecting to come to Pennsylvania and go with her to New York City where Lillian would embark alone for Egypt. She read the letter again. Lillian might get sick, Jennie had written, and not have anyone to take care of her. How like Jennie was this letter. She went on to say that she would help Lillian get settled, then return to America.

"Dear Jennie," Lillian wrote. "I would be delighted to have your company."

But the letter could not be mailed for several days because Lillian did not have a postage stamp—or the money to buy one. However, one day she visited the 42nd street mission and saw a stamp on the floor.

When she handed it to Mrs. Allison who was in charge of the mission, she said, "It is not mine; it must be yours." But Lillian insisted it wasn't hers.

"Well, since it is not mine, it must be the Lord's," Mrs. Allison laughed. "And perhaps He wants you to have it."

The letter to Jennie was mailed.

Finally it was October. Another day and it would be time

for Jennie to arrive in New York. Lillian actually felt ill at the thought of meeting her sister without having the remaining sixty dollars she needed for her passage. Then, another of those strange events, which in themselves appeared to be patterning Lillian's life now, occurred as she stayed at home to rest. She had been sleeping lightly when a knock awakened her. Groggily she made her way to the door, opened it to find a strange woman on the steps. It seemed more a dream to Lillian than reality.

"May I come in?" The voice was eager, the eyes were piercing, stirring, so steady was their gaze. When Lillian had opened the door, the woman stepped in and quietly and searchingly began to ask questions. What were Lily's plans? What was she wanting to do in Egypt? How much money did she need?

Without warning, the unknown little woman knelt by the sofa and closed her eyes. She proceeded to thank God for providing for Lillian's needs. Lillian was puzzled. Her visitor gave no inkling as to what she meant. Then she stood, opened her purse, and handed Lillian sixty dollars and left without a further word.

"Thank you, thank you!" Lillian tried to call her visitor back to express her appreciation. But she was gone as quickly as she had come. "Thank You, thank You!" Lillian was talking to her Lord now. Now she had the exact amount she needed to take her to Egypt.

Now she would be ready when the ship sailed on October 8th.

Now she would be ready to meet her sister, Jennie, the next day.

That night she was invited to speak at a Mission and was

given fifty dollars. Then someone else handed her more after the service. It amounted to a total of seventy dollars above that needed for her passage. She carefully put it away as reserve.

"My God shall supply all your needs," she wrote in her diary that night.

It was a joyous occasion when she and Jennie boarded the ship. Somebody in their party said, "Why don't you open your Bible and read the first verse that you light upon?"

Lillian smiled, but closed her eyes, and opened her Bible. The first verse she saw was one that she had never noticed before: "I have seen, I have seen, the affliction of my people which is in Egypt, and I have heard their groanings, and am come down to deliver them: and now come, I will send thee into Egypt."

"In this unmistakable way God set His final seal on my call," she recorded in her diary that night.

Lillian knew now it must be Egypt forever.

Chapter V

AT DAWN Lillian slipped out of her bunk on the S.S. *Berlin* quietly so she wouldn't disturb her sleeping sister. This date, November 10, 1910, she would never forget. She dressed, put on a warm sweater, and went up on deck. Impatiently her eyes searched for what she knew would be Egypt. Not long after she saw it. The infinitesimal line on the horizon grew and grew before her searching eyes. It swelled almost imperceptibly. But it swelled. Dim and distant though it was, the famed port of Alexandria began to take hazy shape. It was a fairy-tale shape straight from an ancient storybook. As the ancient port swelled into full size, she glimpsed a double-sailed boat floating gracefully at one side. Then another. And another. It was autumn, harvest time in Egypt, she knew. The year 1910 would soon be over. But to her the year was only beginning. All her years were beginning. For in the strange old-new world lay the challenge that had brought her to this port, to this moment. Though recorded Egyptian civilization was old, even ancient, centuries before Christ was born, it was as new to Lillian as this moment in which she was discovering it. And she was ready for discovery.

She looked down at the waters. The gentle, sloshing waters of the beautiful Mediterranean closed in around the ship. Others were crowding around her now for a view of this famous port founded by the conqueror Alexander the

Great more than three hundred years before Christ was born. Like herself, Lillian supposed they had read the history of this land before they came, and knew that this ancient port was relatively new compared to the other cities of Egypt. Now Jennie was standing by her, smiling a trifle grimly, she thought.

"Isn't it beautiful?" she asked her older sister. Jennie shook her head. "Beautiful as you want it to be," she surmised flatly. Suddenly she turned with her old familiar smile. "I like it if you do, Lill." She sighed: "It's just that it's so terribly far from home." Lillian saw Jennie brush quick tears from her eyes, look in the other direction. A moment passed, then Lillian hugged her older sister and said gently, wistfully, speaking personally to the ancient land before them rather than to Jennie: "It *is* home. It *is* home."

Now the sun penetrated the waters with its mighty warmth, sending up rays of reflection. The warmth was a kind of welcome in itself. The famous port seemed to surround them now, its beautiful, circular tiered harbor inviting, cajoling, caressing them with all the sorcery of an ancient and beguiling enchantress. This was the Greek conqueror's "harbor of safe return."

Alexandria was not her destination, though. Nor would it ever be. Beyond, she knew, lay big, bustling Cairo, the Egyptian capital, then the great stone pyramids, the Sphinx, then El Minya, and finally her destination where she knew she belonged for all of her life—Assiout, Egypt.

Not for an instant did she doubt her future and though she did not know what her work was to be, she knew that Assiout, landlocked except for the mighty Nile River, was her own harbor of safe return, because Assiout was where

God had asked her to keep a rendezvous with Him. For eternity. Since she had known this she had moved from one moment to the next, in complete faith, listening, listening —doing only what she felt was her part to getting here to keep that rendezvous. She sighed a little, thinking of the unknown moments, days, years ahead of her.

"Glad You are already here, Lord," she said quietly. Confusion had arisen in the crowd of tourists embarking from the steamer. But a gentle quiet sense of knowing settled over her.

"What did you say, Lill?" Jennie's voice seemed melancholy and far away. Then it moved in more clearly and gently. "What is it, dear?" Lillian felt something warm and soft being pressed against her lips. She forced her thoughts quickly back to her sister as she realized that Jennie was pressing a clean handkerchief against her lips. "If there's any dust, you'll need it, Lill."

Lillian shook her head slowly returning her beloved sister's smile with her eyes. She hadn't noticed dust in the air. How like Jennie to find some little something to do to further their cleanliness and comfort, even at such a moment as this. It was as it always had been: Jennie, dear, loyal, kind, protective, though she instinctively shrank from domination of anyone; Jennie, who had nursed Lillian's bruises and cuts and sympathized and loved her when others didn't always have time; Jennie, who had a passion for cleanliness and orderliness and could not abide a speck of dirt around her house or person. (Once she had scrubbed behind Lily's ears until she had had to doctor the area with iodine when the bath was finished, then had to feed Lily candy for days to salve her guilty conscience.) Jennie was the quiet, sweet, smiling one who loved children passionately though she would never have any of her own. Abruptly Lillian's thoughts went back to the children at Faith Orphanage who always seemed to need more loving and fussing over than they ever got because there were so many to look after and so much work to be done. Faith Orphanage, or any other place where orphans were kept, truly needed someone like Jennie around for the sole purpose of loving. As far as Lillian was concerned, no matter how vast an orphanage, each child was an individual who needed all the love he could get.

"If ever I had an orphanage," mused Lillian as they moved down the gangplank. . . . But the idea of an orphanage seemed so remote that she by-passed it completely. She knew that Jennie had come to this distant side of the world from home with her sister, not because she was duty bound, but because she was love bound. And the latter was the strongest tie on earth. Lillian put her free arm around Jennie now, gave her a quick hug. As she did she looked into the distance of Egypt's clear blue skies which seemed to be higher than any skies she had ever seen.

Now they hurried down the gangplank with the crowd, but Lillian couldn't keep her gaze from going back to that incredibly beautiful sky. Now they heard an insistent voice calling above the din. "Mees Trasher—Mees Trasher!" The sound of it was coming closer. *"Mees Trasher!"*

They turned to find the owner of the voice smiling and bowing. Were they from the United States and going to the Reverend Dunning's mission in Assiout? The young Egyptian's English was almost perfect. His smile was genuine.

And they liked him at once. He pulled out a neatly written message.

Lillian shouted when she read the note. "Kamil!" She shook his hand warmly. "And this is my sister, Jennie. Kamil —Brother Dunning's mission helper—Jennie." Lillian was as relieved and happy as Jennie to see the smiling young Egyptian.

It was a rough but intriguing trip they made across the city to the train which would take them inland to Assiout. The trip was made in an ancient black Egyptian *arabiah*, a horse-drawn carriage piloted by a driver above them in front. The top was pushed back so that they could see the fascinating old world about them. The air was slightly damp, but the sun pushed dramatically through the curtain of dampness, demanding and getting the attention and respect of all. This mighty desert sun was to be the power in Egypt which drove and haunted Lillian and sapped her strength, but at the same time carried her high on its flaming wings toward her goal. But now she was aware only of the strength of it, and the hurrying, milling crowds under it. Now she studied the busy marts swarming with life: the itinerant barber, the water seller loaded with goatskin water bags of his liquid wares fresh from the Nile River, the remarkably beautiful and graceful Egyptian women in their long black garments flowing through the streets in a graceful, compelling rhythm completely foreign to the brisk steps of the women she had observed in America. Lillian felt a deep longing to be a part of the panorama around her. More important, she felt she must get into step with each individual in the scene. No, not just get in step. Becoming one with each of them was her great desire. How could she do it?

Lillian Trasher, left, and her sister Jennie just before sailing from America for Egypt, October 8, 1910.

Lillian as a little girl.

Lillian in 1907.

This picture of Lillian was taken in 1910 after she had been in Egypt two years.

An hour later Kamil had gotten their luggage transferred to the black train. Lillian checked the time. Still an hour before the train left. They began to walk. She thought: "Why, it's just like New York City!"

Indeed it was. The new-old city before them and around them was quite cosmopolitan, the buildings architecturally beautiful. It was like New York City too, in its quick, nervous pace, the noise and confusion, the mingled maze of street languages as Greeks, Jews, French, Arabs, Americans, Englishmen overflowed the streets, everybody hurrying in opposite directions and getting in everybody else's way. Many of the buildings were of brick or stucco, with French balconies and high windows and gingerbread cornices. Around them in the streets they heard cries and shouts, saw bobbing red tarbooshes and long flowing robes of black and white. To one side was a blind beggar calling for help in wailing, cheerless tones, and in every direction were waving hands and sharp eyes. Tangled masses of people gathered and dispersed, as if by signal. Black-gowned women in nose-bag veils brushed by Lillian, Jennie, and Kamil in such profusion that often they were soundly bumped. Now into the older streets. Or were they streets? Crooked, narrow, blind-alleyed—what a contrast to the beautiful modern sections of Alexandria. Now they were hurrying back to the station, boarding the still smoking train that took on passengers from the steamships. This coal-burning train would take them to Cairo, then on to Assiout. Now they were settled as comfortably as possible on the hard wooden seats of a third-class coach.

The massive, teeming commotion accompanying the train's departure was almost unbelievable. Through the wide-open windows the view of the Egyptian passengers pouring like a nervous avalanche toward the train was one Lillian would never forget. The movement was drastic, harsh, tumultuous—men and boys scampering to the windows, tossing their palm reed baskets off their heads and ahead of them through windows into chosen seats, then leaping agilely through the windows and into those seats. On the trip they were just as active, chewing and spitting the sugar cane they took from their baskets when they had ripped the stitches from the burlap coverings. Oh, the myriad collection of items in those Arab baskets: sugar cane, *madammis* (a type of bean Egyptians eat as a breakfast food, Kamil told them), *nabot*, round, flat, hard loaves of Egyptian bread, clothing, jewelry. The Egyptian women wore long black dresses, most of them had silver or iron bracelets on one of their ankles, and all wore black shawls on their heads with small fringed scarves on their upper foreheads. Some wore veils. The men also wore long, protective garments called *gatobias*, Kamil explained, and black camel's-hair caps. Lillian was surprised that not a single Arab man on this third-class coach wore a fez. The poorer men of Egypt never did, Kamil informed them.

The train left the city mostly to one side, followed the sandy ridge that, like a dike, kept out the sea, then rounded the corner of Lake Mariout which Kamil pointed out to them. It then eased past native mud huts hugging the upper shores of the Nile which ran alongside them not far from the railway tracks. The rural countryside was heavily populated, Kamil told them, but it was hard to realize it since the fellahin families were crowded so thickly into tiny mud village houses, each fellah farming his nearby acreage. Each tenant seemed to have an acre—and knew how to make the most of every inch of it. These tenant farmers—"fellahin," Kamil told Lillian, they were called—were an industrious lot, apparently. And Lillian began to like them, even before she knew them.

On the waterfront now they saw a flat-roofed village of narrow, winding alleys, with savage-looking dogs nosing about, apparently searching for bones. The drab huts were without windows and mournful and sagging—built, Kamil explained, of the Nile river mud. Piled high on top of the flat rooftops were cotton stalks and cornstalks, the piles sometimes once again as high as the huts. The squalid sight was tempered somewhat by the beauty of the tall, graceful date palms that seemed to grow in abundance all along the valley. Just away from the tiny village on either side lay the beautifully cultivated fields of rice. Then more fields, flat and still green with alfalfa and maize. Kamil said there were three growing seasons now that more irrigation canals had been dug sixty years before. It got quite chilly here the latter part of December, January, and February, and the nights, especially, grew bitterly cold in the winter when the desert sun went down.

Lillian leaned forward, strained to see the barrage road above. On the Nile River dam was a roadway on which moved a continuous procession of bronzed, handsomely muscled men, straddled over donkeys and followed by women who seemed like lovely dark-gowned phantoms, walking slowly and queenlike in their black trailing garments. The scene was overcast by a glistening golden haze pressing in up the delta from the monstrous marauding desert that seemed to breathe hotly down the neck of the long, slender Nile Valley. Lillian shuddered. What *would* happen if there were no river flowing through this desert, giving the Egyptian people this unbelievably fertile valley?

"What would happen if there were no river?" she asked Kamil, watching the fishing boats, the water wheels at the water's edge being turned by buffaloes which turned the pitchers rhythmically and methodically into the canals to irrigate the fields.

Kamil was smiling indulgently. "Mees Lillian, the Nile never runs dry. It will never run dry. Every year the rains of Ethiopia send the great, raging Blue Nile waters down in floods. The rising water starts in June, goes on through September. The more it rains beyond the Aswan Dam in the mountains, the more the Nile rises down here, and the richer is the silt it leaves to fertilize the Nile valley farm lands."

Kamil pointed out the well-kept fields. "The fellah is a fine farmer. He knows how to get the best from every bit of his soil," he said proudly. A while later they passed an Egyptian fellah working his *shadouf*, which Kamil said was the substitute when there was no water wheel or buffalo to draw the river water. The shadouf was made of a long stick with a heavy rock tied on one end for weight, braced to the ground with another stick forked into the first one. With it, the fellah slowly and patiently could draw water to his crops.

"He had been using these methods—the *shadouf*, the water wheel, the water buffalo—since the days of Moses," Kamil said stoically. "His entire way of living is resignation. He is resigned to this way of life. He has been, forever." Lillian felt deeply this man's passionate love for his people.

"You will be shocked at the manner in which the fellah and his family live, Mees Lillian," he continued. "His conditions and habits haven't changed in thousands of years. It is doubtful if he could change now."

"All things are possible with God," Lillian said firmly. She smiled in remembrance. "Otherwise, I would not be here."

Kamil shook his head sadly. "Ah, Mees Trasher, God perhaps has not been in the fellahin hut." He went on in a dreary tone. The fellah and his family lived in low, windowless huts made of Nile mud, in small rooms together with his goats, sheep, chickens, pigeons, and a buffalo, if he were fortunate enough to have one. The floor was earthen. In these rooms butter was churned, milk was readied for the market, though the fellah's family didn't usually get to use these products because they had to eat cheaper foods, usually cereals. Kamil stopped abruptly and closed his eyes. "Poor fellah out there—he has no chance to rise above his poverty. He has been kept in ignorance for untold centuries."

"His chance is with God," Lillian said flatly, staring out the window now at a group of fellahin struggling to build a new canal from the Nile into a cavernous, rocky cliff. The task seemed Gargantuan, virtually impossible for the masses of fellahin who worked there without any modern machinery. And Lillian told Kamil so. But the Egyptian only shook his head. "Remember, they have been doing this with the same patience and resignation since long before Moses. Think how long they have been developing this resignation." He stopped. Had she heard, he asked, of the ancient Arab verse?

I am going to Syria, said Reason.
I'll go with you, said Rebellion.
I am going to the Desert, said Poverty.
I'll go with you, said Health.
And I, said Plenty, am going to Egypt.
I shall be with you, said Resignation.

Now Lillian's gaze went toward the sky. She was almost overwhelmed with the intense, far-reaching beauty above her. Suddenly she stared in astonishment. The sky appeared golden! She turned to Kamil. He sensed her questions. The gold in the sky? He smiled broadly, looked at the horizon, and above to the great golden sweep. For indeed, the sky *was* gold.

Usually, he explained, it was this way only in the spring when the *khamsin* blew in from the southwest in March, bringing some of the desert dust with it. The khamsin lasted fifty days, generally. Now—yes, he guessed a little desert sand was causing the golden haze, even though it was November.

Lillian glanced at Jennie, who was shuddering visibly. How would her older sister, who couldn't stand a speck of dust anywhere, fare in this land where even the sky seemed to be covered with sand? But if it came only in early spring—

Below the splendor of the Egyptian sky now lay Assiout, nestled in the rich broad span of a green valley at the foot of a sheltering hill. This was the Hill of the Hermits, Kamil pointed out quietly.

It was incredibly beautiful—that first sight. Everywhere were groves of waving palms—indeed, the great palms made a massive wall of green against the sky.

"Nowhere in all Egypt is there such a vista of green," Kamil murmured almost to himself. Such was the picture Lillian now saw before her. For mile after mile, the great expanse unrolled, marked only by the tiny mud villages which appeared as tiny, muddy footprints on the lush carpet of the Nile Valley. Lillian's eyes dimmed with tears. Assiout, climax to everything so far seen, or felt. So lovely did the Coptic city appear to her that Lillian thought for an instant she must have made some terrible mistake and gotten to the wrong spot in the world. How could such a lovely place need her help?

Above the valley city, on the hill, was another city without encircling palms or entrance. Rocky, hilly land spread upward. On it were white domed roofs so delicately pierced and carved as to resemble globes of lace. Surrounding these were thousands of plain oblong slabs of stone, then more lacy minarets, white and perfect, ethereally beautiful in the sunlight.

"Pardon me, Mees Lillian. It is Assiout's city of the dead," Kamil said softly. "Cemetery, I think you call it."

Beyond they saw the city of the living, big and handsome and inviting. For centuries, Kamil pointed out, Assiout had been the home of the Coptic Christians. "Some are descended from those who oppressed the Israelites in Moses' day," he said. He went on, like a child reciting a lesson. When St. Mark founded the first Christian church on the shore near Alexandria, thousands of Copts seized upon Christ's promise of life after death, adapted their festivals to Christian use. "They are a minority group," said Kamil. "Egypt is almost all Moslem."

On the road now Lillian saw four camels, two asses, and a large bunch of children, all heavily laden. They walked slowly in front of a man and his wife, moving their worldly belongings. For an instant, she could see at such close range that she thought she saw a look of fear almost bordering terror in their faces. Then they were past. Later she saw two little girls on the river bank in black skirts playing catch with their veils. Another glimpse and she saw a boy heaving and pulling at a huge camel, trying to get him to the water of a nearby canal. Everywhere she looked the terrain was low and flat and green—with a beautiful golden sky hugging the low green carpet. On the Nile they saw more double-sailed boats—feluccas, Kamil told them—heavily laden, but graceful like great white winged birds coming in from a distance. Lillian would never forget this sight of them. Beyond the graceful feluccas the broad Nile faded before the sweep of the late evening sky, now flashing rose and scarlet and blending and diminishing as it met the golden haze of the desert's horizon. The train was jerking to a halt now: "Assiout," Kamil whispered. "Assiout! Assiout! *Assiout!*" Lillian felt close to tears.

The days that followed passed as an exciting, vibrant dream. The missionaries in their places at the evening meals . . . the Arabic words they kept passing around so Lillian could learn them . . . eating heartily, someone saying please pass the *besara*, Lillian answering *koweis*, which she thought must mean "okay" though she wasn't at all sure. She particularly liked the tall, slender woman who sat next to her —Mrs. Friend, who, with her equally tall, white-haired husband, helped in the mission. They were American missionaries too. And with Sela Friend, Lillian spent many delightful and instructive hours. Together the two women explored Assiout, through the newer palm-lined streets and through the ancient sections of the city. Many times they took Kamil to interpret the strange old-new language for them and visited the market places or went to see Sela's Egyptian friends who welcomed them genially and were always, Lillian found, the perfect hosts. And at the mission Lillian kept up her steady, intensive study of Arabic.

Weeks passed, fully, expanding, and Lillian learned much about the Egyptian people by going among them. How generous they were! More than once she was given dinner when she went to visit a very poor family, only to discover later to her dismay that they had killed their last chicken to serve her a bountiful meal. How they loved their children! Lillian visited one young mother (looking at her girlish face it was evident she couldn't have been any older than Lillian) and though she already had eight children and lived in greatest poverty, she was expecting a ninth child in a few weeks and was overjoyed by the prospect. "Babies are the poor Egyptian woman's greatest happiness," Sela said. "A poor Egyptian mother has nothing—nothing at all but her children. How she does love them! And when she finds she is going to have another baby, even if she has a dozen more, she is very happy."

Winter moved into Assiout. Nights grew cold. When the desert sun disappeared in the evening the night chill began immediately. Lillian and Jennie shivered and huddled together on the hard cotton mattress they shared, trying to keep warm. While she was fervently grateful that her sister was with her, Lillian felt keenly the hardships and loneliness Jennie was experiencing in a land so strange and alien to her. Lillian often heard Jennie crying softly in the night, but knew it was better not to mention it. Jennie, she knew, preferred not to let anyone know just how lonely she was in this faraway land. Jennie had no desire to become a missionary. Lillian knew that her sister belonged in her home in Long Beach, California. Jennie had come solely because Lillian had come, because she loved her daring young sister. Lillian smiled in the darkness, slid her arm around her sleeping sister. How like Jennie was this journey of love. Jennie, who would not step outside in the dark at home in California, had come around the world to try to protect her sister with her love.

Jennie was truly the great one, Lillian thought. She was great in the ways of love. And what greater greatness was there? Where would the world be without the Jennies? If there were none like Jennie who had time to love in a thousand little ways, of what worth would be the Lillians who dared to be bold and fearless? She sighed, snuggled closer to her older sister in the darkness, and went to sleep still gently hugging the dear form next to her.

Chapter VI

LATE ONE Sunday afternoon in February, 1911, a little more than three months after her arrival, Lillian felt a strange sense of foreboding. She couldn't explain it. So she didn't mention it. There was a feeling of death in it. A dreary crying of the wind in it. A wailing of the silence in it. Yet Lillian knew there was no sound here at the mission except for the missionaries' voices. Was the vicious desert sun pushing her off balance?

The brilliant rose hues of the late sun flashed through the small windows, sprayed irridescent light on the heads of the mortals eating their supper, then jabbed and pranced capriciously onto the drab dining table. Mockery, Lillian thought. Irreverent. Such frivolity in the midst of death. She stared at her plate, pressed her palms over her eyes. What *was* wrong with her? In seconds Lillian knew darkness would envelop them. Here in the desert country there was no twilight. Only hot, bright, penetrating desert sunlit skies, almost never touched by a cloud other than the khamsin wind dust clouds which came in March—and nighttime, dark and chilling and mysterious, as only Nile nights could be. This evening Lillian felt a dread sense of expectancy, which, combined with her curious feeling of foreboding, was most unnerving. She ate hurriedly of the besara which she disliked more each day. Suddenly a loud knocking sounded at the door. Lillian jumped to her feet as the door was

75

opened and an excited husky voice, half crying, spoke Arabic in a sharp staccato rush, to the missionaries in the room. Kamil, translating rapidly, told them a young Egyptian mother was dying. Could someone come quickly? Lillian threw her coat around her shoulders before Kamil had finished, and hurried to the Reverend Dunning at the door.

"Let me go," she begged. "Please let me go!" The older missionary glanced briefly at the late evening sky, at the pleading youth before him, then at Lillian. "Well—all right," he said hesitantly. "Kamil will go as interpreter. And —Mrs. Friend." Sela Friend nodded quickly and got her cape as they hurried into the chilling evening air. Lillian turned and kissed Jennie as she hurried out. As she did so, she felt Jennie press a head scarf into her hand. "Wear it, dear," she heard in a whisper.

The three Christians walked in long, quick strides, following the frantic, ragged youth they judged to be the young mother's brother, or husband. He led them past the lovely villas with their massive ornate walls and picturesque palms, then on into another section, poor, tired, and old. Finally, he turned down a dusty path into a small group of mud hovels near the riverbank. They walked in the darkness a few minutes more, then the youth stopped and motioned at the door of a small hovel, barely distinguishable from the others around it. Lillian and Sela Friend followed Kamil and the youth inside, desperately trying to accustom their eyes to the dark windowless interior. Finally Lillian made out the form of a woman lying on some straw on the bare ground. Quickly she knelt at her side, laid her hand on the arm thrown out in apparent abandon of life itself. To her surprise, the young Egyptian mother opened her eyes, looked directly into Lillian's. "*Arjouky, arjouky*," she said piteously. "Please, please, she says," whispered Kamil. But Lillian needed no interpreter to understand the other woman. The two women spoke, and understood, with their eyes. Or was this child really a woman?

Lillian stared now at the eyes she could see clearly for the first time. This one on the straw beside her was only a child. She couldn't have been more than fifteen or sixteen at the most. Now the eyes had turned to look at an object in the dark corner. A sharp wailing cry pierced the air. An arm flailed faintly, weakly. It was a tiny baby, lying in the lap of an Egyptian woman. Lillian looked back at the young child's mother on the ground who lay staring at the infant. She walked quickly to the baby, leaned over to look at it, then shrank back in horror. It was all she could do to keep from running out of the wretched hut to get away— anywhere—from what she now saw. In all her dreams of Egypt she never envisioned such a sight as this.

Lying in the old woman's lap was a baby so thin it appeared at first to be a skeleton. A stench so terrible that it outdid the stench of the hovel surrounded the child, and it was so completely obnoxious that for a moment Lillian thought that for the first time in her life she was going to faint. Then, closing her eyes, she remembered: A smiling face. Words. Words spoken in a soft, sweet voice so familiar that Lillian stopped to listen. "The Lord loves you, and everybody else in the world, Lily, just the way He does Ed and me." For an instant Lillian stared at the face of Anna Mason back in Brunswick, Georgia, saw the big black pot boiling clothes and smelled—not the stench around her—

but Anna Mason's bacon frying in the kitchen and the clean lye soap smell and the fragrant Georgia morning. She saw her friend's smiling eyes and the understanding they mirrored. Lillian opened her eyes, looked down again at the infant—it couldn't have been more than three months old—and smiled as she patted the tiny bone of an arm. To her horror she saw the baby was trying to drink milk out of a can. She looked closer. The milk was stringy and green with age. Yet the starving child was trying desperately to drink it.

Suddenly compassion engulfed Lillian's being in a mighty surge. Gently she reached for the baby, who had now begun to cry. In her arms, the tiny cries faded and the baby turned its hollow staring eyes to her, its little mouth curling and making little sucking, begging noises. Lillian's eyes filled with tears and she felt her cheeks grow wet. Now tears fell on the baby's face and it began the weary little wail of hunger that wrenched at Lillian's heart anew. If she had felt righteous anger at those who had allowed this to happen, it left her completely. This baby wasn't just hungry, as the children at Miss Marker's had been—this baby was starving. Starving to death!

Slowly, carefully, Lillian leaned down and kissed the baby, seeing now the cause of the terrible stench: the baby's clothing was sewn tightly on it. Apparently, it had been this way since the young mother became ill. How long? How long didn't really matter. As she raised her head there was a sound from the straw on the ground. For the first time Lillian was aware that the baby's mother had watched this strange American woman love her baby and show concern for it. It was a universal language, one of love, that passed between the two women now. In the pale light of the moon coming through the open doorway they gazed at each other, each apparently trying to understand. "*Arjouky, takhdihom,*" said the young mother to Lillian. She turned her face away. Then silence. She was dead, Lillian realized, with trembling awe. Except for the baby's wails an eerie stillness pervaded the darkness of the hovel. Again Lillian felt the baby trying to nuzzle its mouth to her, searching, searching, searching instinctively for life-giving nourishment. Lillian hugged the baby closely, feeling more helpless than at any time in her life.

Kamil slowly came to her side, shaking his head negatively. "Mees Lillian," he said softly, "do you know what that young mother said to you before she died?" He looked away, then at Sela Friend standing at Lillian's side. "Mees Lillian, she wanted you to please take the baby home with you. Arjouky takhdihom."

The impossibility of granting the request was as obvious to Lillian as it must have been to Sela Friend and to Kamil who stood silently now. An overwhelming sadness surrounded them. And Lillian felt it permeate even the thick darkness. No one moved, or spoke, for a long while.

"There is no place for a tiny, sick baby at the mission," Kamil said finally. "Brother Dunning would not—well, he *could* not have room. He—"

Where had the youth gone—the one who had brought them here? Husband or brother—whoever he was, he had disappeared into the night.

The Egyptian woman in whose lap the baby had lain now came forward gesturing violently. "*Menfedloch takode el baby,*" she cried in staccato Arabic. "*Arma marifish irmel a beha!*"

"She wants us to take the baby," Kamil translated. "She

says she doesn't know what to do with it." Now the woman threw her arms up. She stepped toward the great river, began to stare at the water in silence. Lillian gasped in disbelief at the thought which came to her. She wouldn't! Yet the old woman continued to stare into the deep waters. Finally she turned and stoically reached for the baby in Lillian's arms, mumbling under her breath. "It's only a girl, anyway," Kamil said, translating her mumbling.

Suddenly Lillian knew the answer within herself. Without stopping to speak to Sela Friend or Kamil she doggedly brushed past the woman, started walking into the night, hugging the wailing bundle to her breast and caring not at all what anyone thought. What she would do with this little one she didn't know. She did know that Christ the baby once desperately needed a room, that everyone, even every righteous one, turned Him away on a lonely, dark, desperate night much like this one, and not so far away from this very land. This baby girl would have a place at the mission. Wouldn't she? Lillian shrank from thinking about it further. If not—well then, she would make a place, somewhere.

Lillian would never be sure how she got back to the mission in the dark that night. A hauntingly lovely full moon shone down on her path and the waters of the Nile, now friendly with her, reflected the moon's guiding light. More than once she stumbled over refuse, rocks in her path, and once her long skirts became entangled with some bushes and she half fell. But never did she loosen her gentle but firm hold on the tiny bundle she had now wrapped in her own coat. The baby girl was asleep now, and stayed asleep even though her trip in the dark was a bumpy one. She was warm, Lillian knew. She could feel the warmth of her own body warming the frail, bony package in her arms.

The hour was late when she slipped in at the mission door, tiptoed to the small shed room she shared with Jennie. If her sister, awake and waiting, was shocked to see Lillian bring in a starving baby, she didn't indicate it. Lillian decided the news of the baby must have arrived earlier with Kamil and Sela. Together Lillian and Jennie warmed some water on the kerosene stove, and while Lillian cut off the stiff, filthy clothing that was sewn on the child, Jennie made some diapers of clean rags and quickly cut out a tiny cotton gown from an old sheet. As Lillian worked she looked up to see Sela Friend, seemingly unsurprised, coming in the door in her gown and robe. Without saying a word, Lillian's friend sat down by the mantle lamp, threaded a needle, and began to sew up the tiny white gown Jennie had cut out. Carefully, Lillian sponged the frail baby, not rubbing at all for fear of injuring the little body. While Jennie held the tiny head, Lillian daubed the cotton cloth to the fine, black hair, matted with mud, human filth, and soured milk. When they had finished, the baby still smelled but the stench was bearable, at least, and Sela began to rock her, singing a soft little baby song and pressing gently between the lips an eye dropper of warm milk, sweetened and diluted with boiled water prepared by Lillian as she had learned to prepare it at Miss Marker's not so long ago. But it wasn't as simple as they thought.

The baby girl, starved and ill so long, could not take the milk. Her cries rose in a pathetic crescendo, went on constantly. Days passed. Nights dragged on. Still there were hours of almost constant crying. The baby girl could not take the sweetened, diluted milk they offered her. She kept losing weight, an ounce at a time, though it seemed to Lillian she didn't have an ounce on her to lose.

The two women took turns walking and rocking the child. Lillian altered the formula, trying again and again to get just the right combination, feeding the baby once every two hours. But still she cried and couldn't take her food. Night after night it was the same.

Lillian was grateful to the Reverend Dunning for his apparent understanding. She knew he was displaying a remarkable amount of patience for a man who was trying to sleep in the house with a sick, crying baby.

Finally the moment came. Tragic though it was, it had to come. Lillian realized that little Fareida, as they called her, was dying in spite of all their effort. The realization came in the small hours of the night. And it grew with the morning. It was a blunt, bitter blow after all the loving care they had given the baby girl. They had made more gowns of the old sheet, cut more diapers, bathed and fed her. They made her a little mattress of her own, rocked her, oh, so carefully. Still she grew weaker. Still she cried endlessly through the nights and went to sleep only because her crying finally exhausted her. Now the mission house was no longer a quiet abode for sleep at night and meditation during the day. Lillian saw that the missionaries who had dedicated their lives to Christian missions in Egypt were worn and haggard each morning. Their eyes were bloodshot from lack of sleep. Little Fareida, though weak in nearly every other way, had excellent lungs!

The first few nights Lillian could tell that they tried not to complain, knowing how much Lillian wanted this baby to thrive. But finally, some one sleepily broke the spell. It was after a particularly long, hard night that Fareida had cried unceasingly that the missionaries came to her in a body and begged her to take the baby back. For twelve nights now the infant had cried almost unceasingly. Lillian stood and faced them pleadingly.

"Back where?" she asked. "She has no place to go." She began to explain about the mud hut, the woman staring into the Nile in the darkness, reaching, reaching for the baby. But her pleadings were futile, she realized. Early that morning the Reverend Dunning called her to his study. He cleared his throat carefully, then looking directly at her said: "I'm sorry, but the mission work must go on. You'll have to take the baby back—immediately."

"But Brother Dunning, there isn't anywhere to take her back to—" Lillian searched desperately for the right words. And for a note of sympathy in his eyes. Why couldn't he see that one tiny baby *was* a mission, that a baby's mind, undeveloped, unprejudiced, and unencumbered with hatred or revenge or malice, could be filled with love and gentleness, compassion and hope and faith in God. God was right here in little Fareida, to Lillian, and all the trouble and disturbed sleep was eminently worth while in her eyes. In God's eyes too, she felt. But the missionary shook his head.

"No," he said. "You'll have to take the baby back—at once."

Tears filled Lillian's eyes and her voice was hollow with emotion as she stood and stanchly faced her superior.

"Back where?" Again she strained to catch a glimpse of sympathy in the man in front of her. "Back where?" Her voice repeated the question like a needle stuck in a groove "Back where? Back where? Back where?" Her mind echoed the short, tragic question. "The baby has no one to go back to. How *can* I take her back?" The minister only shook his head again.

At that moment a decision formed in Lillian's mind, one that must have been coming to her for many days and nights, in the event that this situation should arise. She walked to the doorway slowly. "I will take her back," she said slowly and deliberately. "I will take her back. *And I will go with her.*" She saw her superior's eyes register shock. He frowned, half stood up.

"Alone?" he asked in obvious astonishment. "Alone? An American woman in an Arabic world? Why you'll be killed —or—or starve to death!"

She said firmly: "I won't be alone, Brother Dunning. I'll have God with me."

"Hmm—perhaps. But you'll starve. You have no means—" He was silent then. Finally he looked directly into her eyes. "Very well. But don't expect to come back here. I cannot sanction your actions—if you leave."

Shocked, Lillian stood silent a moment. Then she turned. The missionary closed his eyes, bowed his head, as if to accept her verdict.

Lillian went out the door, headed resolutely up the dirt road.

"That's it," she said determinedly. "I will take her back— and I will go with her."

In her mind was the memory of a narrow three-story house for rent. She had seen it only the week before when she and Sela Friend had gone for baby supplies. Now her steps took her down the long dusty road, her eyes searched for landmarks which would lead her to the house. Finally she saw it and almost ran the rest of the way.

Chapter VII

LILLIAN FOUND the owner of the house a short way up the road. Smilingly he got the key and let her in. There were no electric lights in this old portion of the city yet, so lamps would have to be used in the house. The place was badly in need of cleaning, but the floors were tile and she decided it could be made into a nice abode with some hard scrubbing and disinfectants. Of course there was too much room for just Jennie, the baby, and herself. Lillian paid the owner two pounds for a month's rent, then went to a furniture mart and bought a small kerosene stove for cooking, a table, some chairs, blankets, and a few other items. She would fix the baby a crib out of a box; they could make themselves beds of palm branches. Now she hurried to get groceries and milk.

When she had finished she had used nearly all the precious seventy dollars in savings she had been given at the mission that last night in the United States. But she was satisfied that it had been well spent. Now she walked calmly and purposefully back to the Reverend Dunning's mission house. All that remained was to pack and move. And that would be simple since she owned only a small trunk of belongings and the baby's few clothes they had made so hurriedly could be put in that, also. Jennie had only a large suitcase. Suddenly Lillian stopped walking. Jennie—what would be her reaction to all of this? In the rush of her emotions she had forgotten her older sister, forgotten that she, too, was a part of this new life. By now Jennie would know, she realized. Then, remembering back through the years, Lillian walked on. Jennie had never failed her. Whatever had happened to Lily, Jennie had been her ally. Deeply warmed by the memory, she increased the tempo of her steps, as well as their purposefulness. She had hired a donkey cart and driver to take her trunk and Jennie's suitcase to their new home. And she could carry little Fareida. Now she broke into a little song as she walked. And the melody was a happy flowing thing that seemed to step into her motions as she hurried along, to buoy her up in this great adventure. But it was more than an adventure, she thought soberly. This was God's own doing. It must be!

At the mission she let herself in quietly, half hoping nobody would talk to her. The baby was sleeping and she was glad because it gave her a few moments to tell Jennie of her mighty step personally and to gather her belongings and pack. She had almost finished when she heard the Reverend Dunning's voice in the open door. For an instant, her heart pounded. He was speaking solemnly, perhaps in fatherly concern. She straightened and faced him once more as he cautioned her about making any drastic step for which she would be sorry. He reminded her that here at the mission house she had security, protection, plenty of food, and that she was welcome to stay if she would take the baby back to its own people. Living alone in an Arabic world could mean grave danger for a young American woman, a Christian in the midst of millions of Moslems—and with no money, no support.

"It's all right, Brother Dunning," she said, wishing desperately she could say something to ease his mind. "I don't have any hard feelings. I couldn't. I'm too happy. And I'll be all right. Don't worry. We'll get along fine because the Lord will be with us."

The man turned and walked out, slowly shaking his head. A few minutes later, two of the women came in ostensibly to say goodbye. But Lillian knew they feared for her. It was written on their faces, in their eyes, then in their words. Something terrible could happen, they said, and when Lillian didn't answer they turned to Jennie beseechingly. But she shook her head: "Wherever Lill goes, I go. Where she stays, I will stay," she said softly. Then she arose and as she went to the door with the women, Lillian heard her saying: "Remember Ruth and Naomi in the Bible?" There was a long pause, then, softly, "I guess I am the 'Ruth' in the story." A great warmth filled Lillian. Tears filled her eyes. Oh, to be worthy of such devotion!

When the donkey cart arrived she was ready. As the boy loaded the trunk on his cart Lillian wrapped the sleeping baby snugly. She hesitated a moment wondering if she had enough covers around her. Little Fareida had been undernourished so long that she must not be allowed to get chilled. As she stooped to pick up the baby she felt a light touch on her shoulders. She turned, and her face broke into a happy smile for the first time. There, her arms softly warm around Lillian's shoulders, stood Sela Friend. For a long moment the two women stood and looked at each other, the eyes of each brimming over with tears. Then she saw Sela take her beautiful blue, knitted cape from her own shoulders, and gently put it on Lillian. Carefully, she hooked the catch at the throat. The generous folds fell over the baby in her arms. The soft wool was warm and comforting.

Finally Sela stood back admiringly. "The blue is very becoming to you. If I had knitted it just for you I couldn't have chosen a better color. She smiled. "Take it, Lily," she said. "You'll need it more than I." She put an arm around her young friend gently. "You'll get along fine, I know. But if ever you need me, you know where I am. Remember that, my dear." There was a tight squeeze on Lillian's hand, and Sela Friend disappeared. Now Lillian turned toward the donkey cart and began to follow with long, confident steps. She must get to the rented house while the sun was high. The tiny infant in her arms could never stand the trip through the cold night air. The blue woolen cape was warm on her shoulders, the warmth of it penetrating gently to her heart.

"I'm ready, Jennie," she said, and the two sisters fell into step together.

The trip to their new home was uneventful for little Fareida. Lillian carried her in her arms all the way, and apparently the fresh air and sunshine along the way agreed with the sick child, for to Lillian's astonishment, the baby drank several eye droppers of warm milk soon after they arrived, was able to keep it down, and slept for nearly six hours, something which had never happened at the mission. The weather was cold outside for this was February 10, 1911. But the oil stove and the thick walls of Nile River bricks kept them warm. Little Fareida slept soundly those six hours and Lillian and Jennie huddled together for warmth under the new blankets on their bed of palm tree branches.

When the baby awoke she cried weakly for food and attention, was given both by her benefactors. During the day Lillian increased the amount slightly at each feeding. To their delight the baby began to drink her formula from a bottle a few days later.

Lillian went to bed each night exhausted. But her prayers were prayers of thanksgiving. Tiny Fareida was gaining weight. There were no scales, but it was obvious the baby was filling out. She was drinking her milk readily and the beautiful dark eyes glowed with the brilliance of good health. One morning she looked up at Lillian during her bath, smiled broadly a beguiling little toothless smile, then clasped her adopted mother's hand. Caught by surprise, tears came to Lillian's eyes, but she wiped her face quickly when she saw the look of fright on the baby girl's face. "My little dear," Lillian whispered, "if you only knew what you mean to me!" A quick hug and all was well again.

But not in the kitchen.

Lillian's precious supply of groceries was almost depleted and she had no idea how she would manage for food when it was gone. That night she prayed earnestly for help. This was a crucial test, she knew, of her faith and her future. Could she pass it? Her money was nearly all spent. There was no one to turn to now, no one but God. But she was aware of something she had overlooked before. She knew all at once, looking into little Fareida's beautiful dark eyes, why she had come to Egypt.

She had come to found a Christian orphanage for homeless Egyptian children.

Why had she been so long discovering it?

Lillian sat down at the kitchen table. She had spent the last of her money for the rent and groceries for the month. Now these groceries were gone. The rent was due again.

Yet the knowledge came over her in a joyous wave. She would found her orphanage with faith—not mere money, like Miss Marker back in North Carolina. Her training there, she realized now, had been heaven-sent. She actually knew how to run an orphanage. She had learned how in North Carolina when she didn't even know why she was learning. What was the difference in having an orphanage without funds or annuities in America and in having one the same way in Egypt. That she was alone except for Jennie in a faraway land peopled almost wholly by millions of Moslems did not bother her. She had found she liked the people she had met. She intended to continue liking them. Moreover, she had faith in their good intentions. In herself she had complete serenity, complete oneness of purpose now. She knew beyond all doubt that she belonged here in this Coptic city with little Fareida and any others like her who needed her help.

Eagerly, she told Jennie. But it was Lillian's turn to be surprised. The look of shocked astonishment on Jennie's face was totally unexpected. Her older sister had been sitting alone in a chair by the window. When she heard Lillian's exuberant announcement of her plans, she shook her head unsmilingly. Finally she turned gently to her younger sister. "Lill, dear. I didn't come to Egypt to start an orphanage. I haven't been 'called' as you have. Forgive me, dear, but I am very tired." Jennie walked slowly to the door and looked out for a long while. "I came to take care of you, Lill, to help you in any way I could. I'll keep on doing that though I don't understand how you intend to live—much less feed and clothe children—without money. Without *any* money." A look of fright crossed Jennie's face. She turned and faced Lillian directly. "You realize, don't you, that you have no money at all now." She sighed as Lillian remained silent. Then she continued, shaking her head. "Ah, my dear, if I had your abandon, your complete abandon, it would be different. If I had your faith— But I must face realities—realities such as knowing there is no food for tomorrow, no money to pay the rent which is due in three days. I have faith in God, too. But this faith which holds you, Lily, is beyond me. Beyond my understanding. Beyond my reach."

Lillian stood looking at her sister for a moment, then finally she walked to her side, turned her gently until she faced her.

"I know it is hard to have such faith if it's not in you— if you're not 'called,' as I have been," she said softly. "But have faith in me, in my faith," she begged. "I'll take all the responsibility for the future. Just—just love me, Jennie. You're so good, and so good for me. I'll take all the responsibility." She smiled and hugged her sister. "I know you didn't come to Egypt to run an orphanage. But—it seems I did."

Jennie looked past Lillian wistfully, then smiled slowly and nodded her assent. "But it's your orphanage, your dream. I'll just follow you, Lily."

That morning Lillian had spent her last money for Fareida's milk. In her prayers she explained the situation briefly to God. Of course, God knew all about it. But Lillian wanted to clarify her dependent position in her own mind. She went to sleep immediately after her prayers that night just as if she had a kitchen filled with groceries and money to buy more. In her mind, she already had all of this. What would the morning bring? An answer, she was sure. What answer she did not know.

She was still asleep the next morning when a knock

sounded at the door. Slipping on her robe quickly she opened the door. It was a messenger boy. His note delivered, the boy lingered, rubbing his forehead.

"A headache?" Lillian was solicitous. She had aspirin and offered the boy one. He shook his head fearfully, drinking only the water she had given him. He gulped it down, then went to the door and hesitated again, watching Lillian pick up the baby from her box bed. Then he spoke in Arabic: "Are you the lady looking for children without any folks?"

Lillian was puzzled. Then she remembered. Yesterday at the telegraph office she had told the Egyptian clerk of her dreams of an orphanage for homeless Egyptian children, explaining that she had no money, but the desire to do it with the help of her Lord. Now she smiled, happy that she had been able to understand the boy's question in Arabic. "Yes," she said. And this was her first baby. Wasn't she sweet? She was ill and starving, Lillian explained. The boy smiled for the first time. Fareida reached out her little hand and wrapped it around the boy's finger. Embarrassed, he pulled his hand away.

"Excuse me," he said, then stopped. Then he looked directly at Lillian. "I don't see how—how—"

"Go on, dear," said Lillian.

"What I wondered was—how you going to get the money to pay for this—this?" he looked down, seemingly embarrassed that he had asked the question. Lillian answered him directly.

"Son, my Lord is going to provide for our needs. I don't even know where today's noon meal is coming from. But God does!"

The boy's eyes stared at her, uncomprehendingly at first,

then unbelievingly. Then his stare softened, changed to wonder.

Suddenly he dug into his pocket, then thrust something into Lillian's hand. He turned quickly then and ran out the door.

Lillian looked down to see the first contribution to her future orphanage—seven piasters, the equivalent of thirty-five cents.

"Despise not the day of small things," her Bible told her at the breakfast table. She knew that she could buy bread for a piaster, cereal with another. Then another for milk. How good that food was so cheap in Egypt!

Each day she went out among the Egyptians, told them her plans. Each day she made new friends among them. Yet her mission was so strange, so completely unheard of, that she was misunderstood by a number of those around her. This was particularly true of those she hadn't met. Whoever heard of someone wanting to take homeless children, feed, clothe, and educate them, asking nothing in return? Once a rumor came to Lillian that she was going to take the orphans she sought to care for back to America. Another time she was almost frightened to hear another rumor: that she was going to take children and sell them for slaves. She trembled when she thought of this and deliberately put a clamp on the vein of thought. How discouraging for her sacrifices to be misunderstood, even here where she was trying so hard to follow her Lord's injunctions. Then one day at the telegraph office, the picture changed abruptly to a brighter hue. The friendly Egyptian who worked there told her of two little children in a nearby village whose parents had died. Their uncle would very much like to find them a home. The little boy was four and the little girl was about six. Lillian almost ran home to tell Jennie.

By sunup the next morning, the Egyptian and Lillian were riding their rented donkeys to get the children. Jennie had stayed home with little Fareida. How good the desert world looked to her this morning! Coming home was even more joyful. The children gave her new life, new hope. They were sweet and they were beautiful.

A short time later someone told her of a little orphan boy about five years old. She took him in. There were three children and little Fareida. Lillian was supremely happy because she felt that all was going well. But summer came darkly.

On July 13, 1911, the second day after she took the little boy, he became desperately ill. She hurried to get the doctor from the American Presbyterian Hospital. The friendship of the hospital staff was invaluable. Americans in Egypt became close friends almost as soon as a new countryman arrived. Now the Presbyterian doctor examined the child carefully, took Lillian aside, shaking his head. "I'm sorry. But it's bubonic plague," he said.

Bubonic plague! One of the greatest horrors of Egypt! "No, no, Lord," cried Lillian in desperation. But it was true.

The days that followed were a nightmare. The health inspector sent men to fumigate the house and disinfect everything. The little boy was sent to the isolation ward of the hospital. All Lillian's clothes, curtains, in fact, everything they had was put into large tanks filled with disinfectants. Many of her most vital possessions were completely spoiled.

The second morning later she went in to look at the two other children, now being kept isolated inside the house. She kissed them fondly, then gasped in fear. Hurriedly, she pulled off their clothing, then cried out at what she saw. Red splotches covered their bodies, too.

"Oh, Lord," she fell to her knees and cried in anguish. "What shall I do now? What shall I do now?"

Again the doctor examined her children. This time Lillian sank to her knees in a prayer of thanksgiving. The children, he told her, had the red measles.

She was very tired that night—too tired to sleep, which was extremely unusual for Lillian. It was warm, it seemed —so awfully warm that she felt that something must be wrong. Then she was chilling, then burning, as if a fire were inside her. Finally, gasping for breath and filled with fear, she called Jennie. "I am afraid something is badly wrong with me! Hurry!"

"You have a fever of 106 degrees," Jennie said hollowly when she had taken her temperature. "My dear, if you have bubonic plague, too, I'll never forgive us. Never." Then she came to Lillian's low palm-branch bed quickly and in a low mothering voice entirely changed from the worried tones she had just used, said, "You'll be all right, dear. I'll go for the doctor and be right back."

Lillian nodded, her throat dry, her eyes burning. She was only half conscious as she was carried in a large chair to the American hospital. She barely recognized the faces of Sela Friend and her husband as they helped Egyptian friends carry their load. How did they know? Lillian supposed that Jennie had sent a neighbor for them.

She could hear the doctor talking with Jennie at the door of her room. She saw him pat Jennie's shoulder comfortingly. "She'll be all right." His voice faded to a discreet monotone, but Lillian, listening intently, heard every word. "She's been under a terrible strain," he said. "Let's keep her here for a while and I'm sure she will be all right."

Lillian, feverish and tired, gave up then and went to sleep. What a blessed relief! A few days later her friends carried her home again in the chair. Sela and Jennie had taken care of the sick children as Lillian had known they would. The measles were gone, the terrible bubonic plague had disappeared. Her children were well and happy to see her. "Mama Lillian, Mama Lillian," they called, again and again. And she liked the name.

But she found she was so weak she could not do her work now. "What's the matter with me?" she questioned Jennie. "Is there something I was not told?" Too often, she felt a sharp pain at her heart. When she tried to get up and take care of her children, to do her part of the heavy work, she experienced such weakness and pains around her heart that she had to go back to bed.

But there was nothing wrong. Nothing except weakness, the American doctor assured her one morning. "But," he added, "something could become badly wrong." He eyed her with a firm rejoinder. "Your heart!"

A group of Lillian's Egyptian friends had come with the doctor that morning. Lillian thought that in itself was strange. They had been to visit her often, but not with the doctor. "Lillian," one of them said now, "we think you need a rest. A vacation." She shook her head.

"Oh no, my friends. All I need is to get my strength back so I can go back to taking care of my children again," she said.

One of the thirteen buildings comprising the orphanage at Assiout.

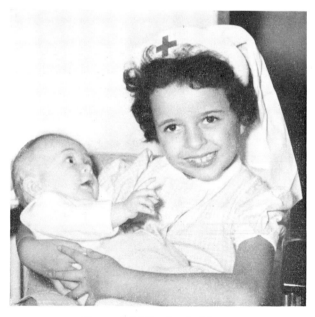

Two of Lillian's children.

Time for a treat from Mama.

Lillian Trasher
as she appears today.

"But that's the way to get your strength back." Lillian shook her head violently. She was being stubborn and she knew it. But she knew there was no time for her to be an invalid. Besides, there was no money for a vacation, so why discuss it?

Now the American doctor was looking at her directly. "Miss Trasher," he said quietly, "you must rest if you are to continue in your work. Your heart has had a serious time of it these last few weeks. How plain must I be? Your heart —your heart could stop beating!" He said, more gently: "I'm sorry to be so blunt. But you must believe me."

Lillian closed her eyes, unbelievingly. Yet she knew what he said must be true. She heard a voice, then, as in the distance. She kept her eyes closed, and listened. For long minutes she listened.

Then another voice, in the room. "Lillian, we have here money for you to take a vacation in Alexandria. The sea air and breeze will do you good, and you can take the rest you need. Jennie and all of us will look after your children."

Lillian didn't open her eyes. She knew she would cry if she did. "To think I had to come clear across the world to find such friends as you," she said softly. "As you say it, let it be."

She took little Fareida with her to Alexandria and the sea air proved a tonic and Lillian honestly tried to rest. After a few days she felt her strength returning, and with it dissatisfaction at being away from Assiout and her children where she knew she belonged.

One evening she took her Bible and knelt by the window overlooking the lovely Mediterranean. For a long time she prayed. Then she opened her Bible at Zachariah 9:15. "Turn you to the stronghold, ye prisoners of hope: even today do I declare that I will render double unto you."

When she arose she felt a great surge of strength in her body, and in her mind—most important, in her heart.

"God has not forsaken me," she said boldly to the Mediterranean waters outside her window. She walked to the baby playing in the middle of the room. "Fareida, honey, we're going to leave here in the morning," she said firmly. The baby girl smiled and raised her arms and Lillian picked her up, hugged and kissed her. "We're going home to Assiout where we belong. To do what we were intended to do. How do I know? I was listening just now and heard God telling me what to do. Trouble before was, I got so busy I forgot to listen."

She began to pack immediately.

Chapter VIII

EARLY IN THE autumn of 1915 an Egyptian friend, Malik, came to see Lillian, his eyes sparkling with excitement. Malik, a government clerk in Assiout, watched Lillian's children busily washing dishes, studying, sweeping, playing, each child content, secure, feeling needed and wanted, and useful. Courteously, he waited until she had finished helping her girls clean some lentils they had spilled. They walked into the parlor; the man looked at her intently. "Miss Lillian, I have news." His smile broadened; his voice lowered. "The half-acre across the Nile that you wanted is going up for sale." Lillian looked at him in astonishment. "I thought the owner wouldn't sell," she said flatly. "You know how I've tried—"

"Now it belongs to a very fine lady, Miss Lillian. She will sell it for fifty pounds."

"Fifty pounds! Malik, that's a fortune to me. How could I—"

Her friend kept on, though: "I thought if you could be first—" He went on to tell about the new owner and what she had told him. As he talked Lillian's eyes suddenly became alive. She had heard of the new owner, Mrs. Amina Khyat, and realized that she was a good Egyptian friend. She studied the face of her young Egyptian friend. Fifty pounds. Two hundred anf fifty dollars in American money. Now her eyes glowed as she felt a tremendous sense of fulfillment of purpose. She smiled and in a soft voice said: "Ah, yes, Malik. And my dear children could have a home of their own. How I've dreamed of such a time." She sighed, sat down slowly. "Let's see who might help—" Lillian's mind went back to her Egyptian friends who had helped her in the past. How kind the Egyptian people had been once they understood her purpose in their country. She had learned early that she must go to them, rich and poor, for money, food, and supplies, to explain that she was taking care of homeless Egyptian children, but that they would have to provide the money because she didn't have it. The small gifts from the United States didn't begin to cover even their simple needs. They could never have gotten by at all if living hadn't been so cheap and their wants so few. Food, just enough clothing, the quaint, narrow three-story house she rented so reasonably. Jennie, Lillian, and her children, now eight in number slept on palm branches, ate besara, rice, a few vegetables and had their pleasures together playing, working, praying, reading the Bible, studying English in daily classes which Lillian taught. Jennie had gone back to the United States the year before to look after her rental property in California and had returned recently feeling very happy at being back with Lillian and the children whom she dearly loved. Lillian was sublimely happy. When food ran low (which was a regular occurence every two or three days), she learned that she could rent a donkey for three piasters, then go on the little animal to a nearby village for food supplies which the generous fellahin always provided. Wheat, beans, onions, rice—whatever the farmers felt they could live without. Their giving meant hard sacrifice. Still they always looked forward to her next visit on the donkey and tried to have something for her children, no matter how small the quantity. The fellahin were generous-hearted though circumstances had forced them into living so frugally that it was almost incredible to Lillian that they could survive at all.

The fellahin villages not on the fertile Nile River bank huddled on the desert fringes, the only other place to live in Egypt, with no protection from the raging heat of the desert sun. The windowless huts were like cold storage vaults in winter and in summer were like brick-baking kilns. Lillian often wondered how they stood it. Besides this, they generally kept their farm animals inside their houses. It was a long time before she realized that they had stood these conditions century after century with the same resignation Kamil had noted in the beginning of her Egyptian life.

But hope and faith in the future were a part of Lillian and her Christian beliefs. She could be resigned to the hopeless only when she could not change circumstances with the backing of her Lord. Here on this half acre Malik had virtually bought her this morning she could help build the Kingdom of God and fill it with her beloved Egyptian children, teaching them the way of her Lord the Christ and His great promise of rich, meaningful lives under His care and Heaven beyond their earthly lives. Suddenly she jumped to her feet.

"Malik, we'll do it! Go tell Mrs. Khyat her money will be ready in a—a week." Malik hurried out to accomplish his mission his face alight with happiness. Lillian quickly went to her bed of fronds and knelt beside it. "Lord, show me the way," she asked. "I'll need the money—all the money in a week. I have twenty-five piasters (a dollar and twenty-five cents) in the house. But if this is Your will, show me the way. . . ."

Quickly she went into the kitchen, told Jennie she was leaving, then almost ran to the donkey stables. On the donkey's back, she calmed herself, fell easily into the jerk-sway donkey motion as the quick little hooves tapped down the road, and prayed earnestly: "Show me the way, Lord. Show me the way."

The "way" led to the *mudir*, the governor of Assiout. Into his luxurious offices she now walked boldly. A plan had come to her as she rode her donkey. And, as was her usual custom, she wasted no time getting into action once she was convinced the instructions were from her Lord and not from her own creative mind. She had been told that the mudir was interested in her plan of a home for Egyptian orphans. This, she was sure, was the time to further that interest. So she went to meet him. In her mind, also, she was remembering a well-to-do Egyptian man who had stopped and watched her children at play a few weeks before. When he left he gave her his card. And she had been surprised to note that he was an official at the police station in a nearby town. He had left money to help feed her children and told her he would help her again. How Lillian had appreciated his kindness! The eight growing children she now had needed lots of food. That took money—a commodity she never seemed to have in adequate amounts. Perhaps this kind friend would help her again in this great emergency. Somehow she felt impelled to go to him with the backing of the mudir. And this was an excellent opportunity to meet the mudir and seek his cooperation. Would he see her? She studied the luxurious interior of the reception room. Then the door opened.

She was being ushered into the executive's private offices. Lillian sat down and began to tell him of her plans. As she talked she could see the Egyptian official was listening with increasing interest. Finally she told him of her immediate need and of the man in the government office in a nearby city who had told her he would help her if the need arose. Now it had. She needed fifty pounds to purchase the half-acre plot to build her orphanage. She had nothing. She would like to go with the mudir's approval. Would he be kind enough to make an appointment for her?

The mudir smiled now. Indeed he *was* in accord. Yes, he would call the man and arrange an appointment. Did she have transportation?

"Yes, my donkey," smiled Lillian. "I go out all the time to the villages to get food for my children—always on a donkey."

The man's face registered surprise, then consternation. He frowned. "A young American woman alone on a donkey in the desert? It's incredible," he exclaimed. "Haven't you ever had—haven't you encountered—" He looked down at the floor, suddenly embarrassed.

"No," Lillian smiled, "I haven't." There was a long silence, reminding her of the time she first told the Reverend Dunning of her dream of going to Africa as a missionary without support. "I'm not bothered by anyone," she said simply. Egypt has given me only kindness." She looked intently at the mudir who was now studying her with a puzzled expression. "You see," she concluded, "I'm not really alone out there on my journeys. My Lord is with me every moment." She hesitated, seeing the strange look on the face of her listener. Then she saw him relax and smile benevolently. "As you say it, let it be," he said. "Miss Lillian, all of these good things I have heard about you are true. That is quite plain." She stood to go. As the mudir rose he said, shaking his head resignedly: "But on a donkey! How degrading for a very attractive young lady! A donkey is a symbol of utter baseness, of ridicule—"

Lillian stopped halfway to the door and turned. "A donkey was good enough for the Mother of my Lord. It's certainly good enough for me." She laughed ruefully. "I guess I'm the lady on the donkey. I've heard the fellahin call me that when they see me coming."

The mudir smiled, then began making a note on his desk. "Will eleven o'clock in the morning suit you for your appointment?"

"That's perfect," Lillian answered. "Tomorrow."

"Then I'll call the gentleman." He hesitated, then wryly: "I suggest that the lady on the donkey hire native donkey drivers and that the party leave at dawn in the morning. That's a long trip for a young American woman to make alone on a donkey."

Lillian left filled with joy. The mudir had been most co-operative. She liked the man greatly and hurried her donkey toward the stables as fast as she could and hired two donkey drivers to guide her on the trip the following morning. Actually, she had made the trip alone many times on a donkey, but never so far during the flood season. Since this was July and nearing the peak days of the great river's annual flooding, the water would have spread across the land on each side changing vast areas into deep and many times dangerous swamps and lakes. It would take clever donkey drivers indeed to lead the way on this journey.

Long before dawn they were on their way. The drivers beat on the donkeys lightly and the quick, machinelike beat of the tough little hooves on the desert sand was a sweet song vibrating through Lillian with each step. By sunrise they were well into the low country and were having to take long desertwise detours to escape the far-reaching waters which crawled over the land like the air itself, leaving the canals overflowing and the earth useless until the excess water soaked into the ground or was evaporated by the hot desert sun. Lillian knew that the silt the flood waters brought down the Nile would fill the canals, making it necessary for Egypt to clean out the stopped-up waterways when the season was over. In the past, Egyptian friends had told her that the fertile silt had been a wondrous blessing, making the soil the richest in the world. But now the fertile silt was a great hindrance. Since time began the rich earth had been brought down annually by the floods from the high regions beyond the great Aswan Dam. Up there it was a raging torrent, wild, treacherous, destructive, a roaring spectacle of mighty wrath on the loose, respected, worshiped, feared. This was the powerful Blue Nile above the Aswan Dam which sent its mighty waters down to Egypt. But here the water was a sleeping giant, swelling soundlessly throughout the summer months and usually becoming its greatest in September, lying alongside and often islanding the tiny Egyptian villages.

Now they found themselves weaving in and around the canals, often swinging far out of their way into the desert to get away from the still but potent water. They were trying to ease back closer to the river to shorten their route when Lillian looked at her watch. Eight o'clock! According to her calculations they were running behind schedule. Since the flood waters were causing them to go farther out of their way than she had expected, only a little more than three hours were left until the eleven o'clock appointment. One thing she knew: She could not be late! A home for her children was too important. She urged the donkey drivers to hurry as much as possible. Then she relaxed, tried to think calmly. They were making better time now, she thought reasonably. If no more detours were encountered surely they could make it all right. A few minutes later she wasn't so sure.

With cold dismay she looked ahead to a vast swampy area. The water didn't appear too deep, but its scope was broad. She got off her donkey and studied the area. She felt it was much too far to go around the broad expanse of water and still keep her appointment. On an impulse she sat down and took off her shoes and stockings. Her ankle-length skirts worn by women of that time would be a little hard to keep out of the water, but she figured she could manage. Certainly she had had enough experience as a child wading in and out of the ocean tides in Jacksonville and Brunswick. Surely she could wade through a swamp that was obviously shallow. She began to walk into the water, but stopped an instant, hearing the two donkey drivers calling her. Respectfully, they had wandered off a little way as she had taken off her stockings.

"Wait! Wait!" Their voices were sharply Arabic in their obvious concern. "Wait, Mees Lillian," the larger one cried. "You'll have an accident!" But Lillian had no time to wait.

The boys called again, insisting they should go around the water. But Lillian kept going. Time meant nothing whatsoever to the Egyptian donkey drivers. They didn't understand the importance of being on time this morning. She did. The future of her children was at stake. Once more the boys called to her. They would make a pack saddle, they said, and carry her across on their arms. She shook her head impatiently. "I'll carry myself across. Bring the donkeys and come on!" She became bolder then, walking faster. The water got deeper and she was forced to raise her skirts almost to her knees. She glanced back at the boys, smiled briefly at their shocked faces. Then she took another step, her confidence soaring—and plunged.

Into the muddy residue and clammy water she went with a mighty whoosh! She seemed to go at once in all directions and had the ridiculous feeling that she would never be able to gather herself into one body again, even if she were able to pull herself free of the mud and filth which now almost covered her. Pulling herself free with the help of the donkey drivers, she finally made it back to dry land.

"I must have gotten into the canal," she said sadly. "Water was over it and I couldn't see it. The donkey boys just shook their heads. "Guess we should have gone around the long way, as you said, eh? Or tried the pack saddle." The problem, though, was not what she should have done, but what she could *now* do with her clothing soaked with fertile Nile mud.

In her suitcase on the donkey was a dry blouse and skirt. But no change of underskirts without which no lady of the day could be seen in public. "Lord," she prayed miserably. "I've made a fool of myself. I need help. I can't go this way to see an important man. And I must go or I won't have the money ready to pay for our orphanage land. There's less than a week to raise it and—" Suddenly her eyes lit on a small shack made of cornstalks. At the entrance a woman stared at them in astonishment. "There's my answer," Lillian said and began to walk toward the Egyptian smiling, though she knew the mud made her smile something less than beguiling.

Yes, the woman would help her if she could. As Lillian expected, she was treated hospitably. But the woman shook her head when she asked for water to clean up. No water except that in the earthen bowl where her ducks bathed. Lillian was nonplussed. When they finally persuaded the ducks to get out, she immediately started scrubbing the muddy underskirts without soap in dirty water.

When they were as clean as possible, the two women spread them out on top of the cornstalks. The sun shone warmly but Lillian realized now they would never make it if they waited for the underclothes to dry so she could wear them. For the first time that day she felt tears welling up in her eyes. But, dressed in her fresh blouse and skirt from the suitcase she decided to explain the problem to her donkey drivers. Humiliating, of course. Unladylike. The idea of discussing such feminine troubles with donkey drivers. But no matter.

Moments later, they were on their way again, this time traveling safely around the big swamp. In front of her the donkey drivers forced their animals into a brisk trot, for a wonder. And held high on a clothesline made of long date palm branches the boys had made hastily, Lillian's underskirts billowed brazenly but beautifully in the warm sunshine and the breezes created by the trotting donkeys.

Lillian smiled: "The ways of the Lord—and the donkey drivers." When they arrived the underskirts were fairly dry, though a different color from the white they were when the trip was begun. Finally, she found a private spot to slip on the underclothing, though that was a task in itself on the desert.

At eleven o'clock she walked into the police station offices, found a cordial welcome, and was given most of the money she needed so badly for her new orphanage ground. She thanked her benefactor warmly. Then, "Thank you, Lord," she said silently. "Thank you, boys," she added aloud to her donkey drivers.

They took the long, safe, dry road home.

The transaction on the orphanage half acre was finished at noon two days later. Now she and her eight children could call the wondrous land their own. She had been given enough money by various Egyptian friends to finish making up the fifty pounds needed. Only a few piasters had been left over. These, amounting to less than a dollar in American money, she carefully put away. In her mind she could picture quite easily a lovely white brick and stucco orphanage with a protective wall around it, an open courtyard inside for prayers and Bible reading in the evenings when the day's work was done. There would be lovely trees and masses of flowers in the courtyard to nourish the beautiful in their souls while they worshiped God with their prayers. The great wall around the building would have a massive front gate. Lillian could see the gate clearly, even now. It was open, open always to homeless and unwanted Egyptian children. Perhaps the numbers might increase until there were twenty-five or thirty in the orphanage someday. For an instant, Lillian caught another glimpse. It was an awe-inspiring glimpse—one which almost frightened her. In that instant she saw a thousand children coming through the great open gate. Their bodies were pitifully thin, their clothing in rags, their eyes dark and beseeching, looking up to her, their thin arms reaching out to her as they entered. Suddenly her eyes peered behind them. There in the distance she could see a line that reached clear to the desert's horizon. There must be thousands coming in the distance! Lillian closed her eyes, crying softly. "I've seen all I can see in one look, Lord. I can't stand the wonder of it any longer." She walked briskly to the half acre and began to pace off the outside walls of the building. It would have to be large —a dormitory for boys and one for girls, a big kitchen and dining room and a nursery.

Two stories high, with the customary flat roof nearly always used in Egypt. It was a beautiful structure, Lillian thought, walking across the land. It was as clearly visible to her as if the building and wall were finished. Suddenly, she turned and began to walk toward the rented three-story house where her children waited with Jennie. She began to run, faster, then faster. Inside, she called the children to her. "We'll start making bricks next week," she said joyfully. "Our older boys can work at it and we'll all help in the best way we can. Even the little ones can do something."

Lillian saw the puzzled looks on the faces of her oldest boys. "Don't worry, John. We'll get someone to help us," she said. "And the Lord will show us anything else we need to know. You know, children, the Lord knows all about making bricks. And He wants us to live in our own home."

She hesitated an instant, then smiled and whispered: "I know because He told me so!"

Lillian laughed when friends questioned her about her building plans. She would begin the orphanage buildings, she said, if she had three bricks. Then a big laugh. "And I have three bricks."

At the beginning those bricks were not easy. But had the Lord promised her a life of ease?

They began the brickmaking early in September, 1915. How bright and hot was the sun! Far to the back of their plot she could see the Nile overflow waters inching toward them. But they were safe from the annual floods, she knew. Long ago she had found that the Egyptians were wise in the ways of the Nile. They knew almost exactly how high the waters would come each summer. And they built accordingly. Across the Nile she could see the city of Assiout, palm lined, beautiful, and high above flood danger. She, too, felt high above flood danger—above all danger.

She brushed a strand of hair from her eyes, then hesitated when she saw a loose hair which clung to the mud on one of her hands. She stared at it a few seconds, then smiled. The hair that had fallen was white—her first one. She didn't feel old, she thought. She was still in her twenties. She sighed and deliberately patted the white hair into the wet, black mud which filled the wooden forms, then looked beyond at the results of their labors.

The hot September sun shone on row after row of wooden forms, each holding twenty bricks. How lovely to behold! Spread out far across the vacant half acre, the mud-filled forms made a picture of rhythm and order. To her eye it appeared as a vast patchwork quilt with a shining black diamond gleaming from each little rectangular block. It had been easy once those forms were built and they had learned how to mix the ingredients. It was simply a matter of digging the dirt, placing it in a pile, and adding water from the river, straw, and manure to get the right consistency. Then John and his younger helpers would jump into the mixture, arms and legs beating, stomping, stirring, kneading. When it was thoroughly mixed they each got a handful and carried it to the forms, then another, and another. Then it was packed in hard and smoothed. Even the smallest ones carried their share, load after load cupped in their small hands. Mama was filled with pride in her children as she watched them work.

The desert sun was burning furnacelike, today, the intense heat far greater than the worst summer heat she had known in Jacksonville, Florida, Brunswick, Georgia, or Boston, Massachusetts, as a child. Americans couldn't possibly understand the terrific summer heat that Egypt knew. Heat of 105 to 120 degrees was normal and expected. Those were the days that hurt her most. Traveling on her donkey through the burning desert was one of her greatest ordeals through the years. The heat was a demon that fought her savagely, beat her down until she cried out for mercy, condemned her when she failed, laughed at her fears, scorned her mightiest efforts. This ugly demon appeared early in June and haunted her through September of each year. If she could have stayed inside she could have stood it more easily, perhaps. The thick walls of the Egyptian buildings formed a barrier that kept the demon heat partially at bay —though it was bad enough inside. But out in the desert, unprotected on a donkey's back, the heat was almost unbearable.

Hour after hour, day after day, year after year, winter and summer— there could never be a letup in her foraging trips through the desert for a very simple reason: Her children must have food daily, whatever the season. As in the past she knew she would have to continue to travel on her donkey through flood times, hot dry times, cold winter times, khamsin sand dust times— Through the years past it had been. And so it would be for years to come. She simply accepted it as her lot.

She shuddered as she thought of those khamsin days.

Even winter in Egypt seemed easy compared to the khamsin winds of early spring. Winter was bitterly cold here. One stopped to visit a friend. There you sat, each of you wearing two sweaters, a heavy coat, a heavy scarf on your head, three pairs of socks on your feet, heavy shoes. Even in such terribly cold weather, the homes of the Egyptian poor were virtually unheated. The American missionaries who came and went through the years in Egypt suffered in the winters from chilblains and had to use heavy wraps to stand the weather. Truly there seemed to be no place so cold in January as the interior of the unheated mud house. In the orphanage, the kitchen was warmed by the heat of cooking. And in later years one of Mama's missionary helpers built a fireplace in their quarters. But the penetrating cold didn't bother Mama especially.

Winters in Egypt were easy compared to the khamsin season of wind and dust in the early spring. At this time the khamsin winds from the southwest pounded and whipped Egypt with desert sand which penetrated every crack, every corner into the kitchens, into the dishes, into the food, the clothing, even into the people—their ears, eyes, skin—until the desert sand and the people in it seemed to be one.

But the springtimes in Egypt after the khamsin season were beautiful. Great flowering acacia trees, bougainvillaea blossoms on high iron grill fences or on picturesque walls, the lovely villas inhabited by charming gracious hosts and hostesses, and always the stately date palms high in the cloudless blue sky like great green-capped cathedrals. All of this, and the mighty, beautiful Nile eternally flowing through the slender Nile Valley, winding gracefully, enchantingly, peacefully through its allotted course in season and then overflowing in season, as if according to an almighty plan. How powerful and good was this river God had given Egypt! How beautiful it was in the springtimes when the khamsin winds went back to the far southwest desert and left the lovely Egyptian countryside again in peace!

Summer, the time of the demon heat, was a beautiful time, too. But the intense heat of the desert made it impossible for Mama to appreciate the scene around her, especially on her donkey in the desert.

She recalled now the donkey journey she had made a few weeks before. Knowing of the money they would need for the building, she had scheduled a full day of travel on her donkey in the desert. Eleven fellahin villages. The thermometer in the shade at the orphanage had registered 116 degrees the day before. Today seemed even hotter. But eleven villages could mean help that would lay bricks, buy doors and hardware, not to mention the food and clothing. She had left before dawn to try and get ahead of the demon heat. She arrived at the first village without difficulty. The dawn air was refreshing. Then the sun was exploding its blazing onslaught in a mighty moment that changed refreshing, dark night into a shimmering, glaring, aching desert day.

The villagers gathered. From house to house they all went, as they had in the past. Each gave what he could. Then she was on her donkey again in the desert.

Another village.

More miles of desert heat.

Another village.

To the desert again.

And another village.

Late that night she visited the eleventh one. It had been a wonderful generous day. How thankful she was for her fellahin friends in the villages! How exhausted she was though. She was so spent from the heat that she felt she would burst into tears if she couldn't get some quick relief. She felt she could hardly climb onto the board bed which she knew would be provided at the police station. She pressed her palms over her aching eyes, but felt no relief. Her hands were burning too.

Finally, they were at the police station. She felt she couldn't take another step if her life depended on it.

But she was due a surprise. The jail was occupied. For once there was no room even in the village jail for a lady and her donkey.

Her village host, seeing her exhaustion and seeming to understand, told her to come to his house. His wife would make a place for her. Somehow she made it to the villager's one-room mud house. Her head, her eyes, her whole body burned. Her entire being seemed on fire with the terrible heat she had endured under the desert sun.

She fell onto her bed on the earthen floor thankfully, praying for quietude and a breath of coolness. Then, to her astonishment she felt the small breath of air from the door opening cut off as her host made the little house ready for the night. She remembered then. The fellahin families always closed up every opening against the night. For protection perhaps. Or habit. At any rate, the fellah, his family, his farm animals always seemed to shut themselves up each night, no matter what the weather was outside.

Now her host went to the small kerosene lamp on the table. Ah, he was going to turn it out. Mama breathed a sigh of relief. The globeless lamp, which smoked badly, had already filled the stifling windowless mud hut with fumes and smoke, not to mention the increased heat it gave off. But no—he wasn't turning it off. He was cutting down the flame for the night. The problem would become worse instead of better as the night wore on. She groaned in misery. Now to one side of the room bells tinkled. At first she couldn't find the source. But a while later she understood. The fellahin baby had bells on its fingers and toes. It began to cry after a time and each time it moved its hands and feet, the bells sounded. The sounds, which ordinarily would have been pleasant, happy tones to her, felt like sharp, hot knives in her burning ears. She remembered vaguely Paul's prayer during a hard night. "When will this night end, Lord?" she cried wordlessly. There was an echoing jingle of bells, this time she realized, from the family cat which also wore bells around its neck.

But the building materials would be ready for Misregee,

the bricklayer, now, because she had gifts from eleven villages in her bag.

It took her several days to recuperate from the effects of the desert heat this time.

A few days later, they lifted off the wooden forms. Now the bricks were a brownish gray. They were hard, heavy, and beautiful. She and the children carried the precious parcels to a clear spot and carefully stacked them. How well they worked when they had a chance to learn! Always she would remember the little boys hugging a single brick to their bodies as they walked, the older ones proudly cupping the bricks, three in each arm as Misregee had taught them. How careful they were! When one had to make bricks by hand one certainly carried them carefully.

"Are you ready to start digging a new load of dirt?" Mama called. The Egyptian boys grinned, mopped their brows, and began to dig. They were tired and hot under the merciless desert sun, she realized, but wouldn't admit it. Now she saw a familiar form coming down the road. Mama sighed happily. Misregee, the man who was to lay the bricks, was coming by on his way to Assiout as he did every noon. Now he greeted her as he walked. She smiled broadly. "All is well, Misregee, I think. How do they look?"

The husky, broad-shouldered Egyptian walked to the stack of homemade bricks, picked up one in silence and examined it critically. Then he nodded and smiled. Finally he said: "If your boys had been making bricks all their lives, they couldn't look better." "Ah," said Mama. "The forms you helped the boys make—how can we ever thank you enough?"

Misregee shook his head and waved an arm horizontally in quick, sharp motions. "No thanks needed, Mees Lillian. It is we of Egypt who thank you." They talked briefly of the foundation. The boys could dig it when Miss Lillian had the plans finished, he said. He would help mark it off. Were the plans drawn?

Mama shook her head with a laugh. "Misregee, I never drew a plan. I never saw anybody draw a plan. I've worked for days trying to get it just right. Oh, the paper I've used— and thrown away."

It was true. She had worked far into the night for many nights by the light of a kerosene flame. She figured on four full beds (made of boards, of course) in each room. The mattresses, if they had mattresses, might be made of palm fronds until they could do better. But that didn't matter. She calculated the size of the four beds very accurately, then drew the room around them—to fit the beds. Since the walls would be more than two feet thick as was the custom in Egypt, a large cupboard for clothes and belongings could fit nicely into the wall of each room. There had to be one room for the girls and one for the boys. There must be a kitchen, a visitor's room, and one for herself. All these rooms should be built about an inner courtyard. The courtyard, thereby completely enclosed, would be a wonderful, private place for play, evening prayers, and outdoor living room, a place to eat in warm weather. And there would be two great trees in the courtyard—beautiful flowering acacia trees, if she could find two little ones to plant. And she knew she could. Mrs. Khyat, her good Egyptian friend, had some tiny ones growing on nearby strips of land. Mama knew all she would have to do would be to ask her for them.

The first building would have to be one story, she concluded, rather than the two-story structure of her original dream. A second story could be added later if it were needed. The walls would be made of the homemade mud bricks which her boys were making each day. There would be several rows of these needed to make the thick walls, then the outside wall of these would be heavily plastered and painted ivory. The flat roof would be made of palm tree trunks placed very close together, one end placed on the outer building wall, the other on the nearest courtyard wall. By having no roof over the courtyard, the span of each supporting palm trunk would be shorter and, thereby, stronger. On the palm trunks a mesh of smaller palm fronds would be laid out. And on this the mud would be packed completing the roof. All this her Egyptian friends had explained to her, Kamil in the beginning, and now Misregee, who had agreed to work on the building by the day. When she had the money to pay him, they would go ahead. When there was no money, he would wait until she was ready again. What a kind friend to Mama and her children!

"We're almost ready for you, Misregee," she told him now. "The boys can dig out for the foundation. Do you think we have enough bricks made for the foundation?"

Misregee shook his head negatively. "Mees Lillian, you cannot use these bricks for the foundation, I am afraid."

Mama turned in surprise. "Why not? Aren't they good enough?"

Misregee smiled. "They're good bricks. But they're mud. You should have a foundation of strength. You need real bricks from the factory here. Then we can lay the mud bricks on top of them."

That sounded reasonable. Mama realized that her Egyptian friend knew building and what was needed to make the new orphanage sturdy and sound.

"I will order them, Misregee," she said simply. She had to smile to herself. She had said it so easily: *I will order them, Misregee.* Just as if she had even a piaster with which to buy them.

"It will take about three pounds for that many, I'm afraid," Misregee said.

Mama frowned. "So much?" Then she smiled, and turned quickly. "I'd better go pray." It was said more to herself than to Misregee. Her steps were quick and sure. She knew she must have the good bricks first. In her room, she knelt silently. Then, without preliminaries: "Lord, shall I order the factory bricks now—or wait for the money?" Carefully, she listened. Then she hurried to Assiout and ordered the bricks for the foundation.

Early the following morning Mama and an Egyptian soldier the mudir had offered for her protection were on donkeys headed for the fellahin villages. Mama felt strongly that she must get the brick money so she could pay that bill promptly. Also she would need money to pay Misregee and his workmen each day. Now that they were almost ready to begin actual construction nothing must hold them back. Not even the powerful Nile flood waters.

They were about three miles from their goal, which was the village of Kom Es Fat, when they were forced to slow down. For nearly a mile they had been traveling through shallow water. Now they turned to one side, finally stopped. It was not safe to go farther toward Kom Es Fat. Yet they

must get there. But how? Flood waters completely surrounded the tiny village. It was an island to itself, tiny,
lonely, remote, but beautiful to Mama, in the distant glare
of the bright sunshine. In those crowded mud huts, Mama
knew were kind-hearted fellahin families who would help
her despite their extreme poverty. Mama and the soldier
detoured to a nearby village and began to inquire about a
boat. Obviously, it was the only way.

By noon they had found one and rented it. It was a flimsy,
makeshift thing, but apparently would be capable of cover-
ing the two or three miles of water between them and Kom
Es Fat. Now the boatman, the soldier, and Mama were on
their way. The boat seemed to be safer in the water than
it had appeared to be. The boatman was quite competent,
too.

In the village, the friendly fellahin gathered, as they
always did, when she arrived. As she expected they were
generous with the little they had. But she was genuinely
amazed when she was ready to go and counted their gifts.
They had gathered enough among themselves to total five
pounds—enough to pay for the good bricks and also enough
to pay Misregee and his workers for about two days. Tears
came to her eyes when she saw how needy they were, yet
how generous. Now the foundation would be laid at once.
And when that was done, there would be no stopping them.

Carefully, she tied the money in a cotton bag. The sun
was almost down when they shoved off. There was a slight
wind which seemed to increase in velocity as they moved.
But it wasn't strong enough to cause alarm, apparently.
They moved into the water easily despite the wind and
Mama settled down happily. Moments later she was aware

of increasing winds, higher waves. A short time later she felt a quick jerk, then a blast as a sheet of wind threw the boat to one side. In the near-darkness it was a terrifying motion. Mama and the soldier grasped the sideboards in a desperate attempt to stay upright. "Lean the other way," she screamed. It was fortunate that they did for almost immediately another wall of wind struck sending the old boat careening almost over. Somehow the old craft groaned and heaved back upright. Darkness had settled heavily over them now. But moments later the penetrating rays of the full moon shone through to them. Somehow, that helped Mama. At least they could see their plight now. Perhaps someone else would too.

By the light of the moon, she tied the precious five pounds she had been given to her underclothes. "If I drown," she told herself grimly, "they'll find the money for those foundation bricks."

Now the wind had quieted. Perhaps, she thought, the worst was over. But it was a false quietness. Another blow seemed to hit from below, lifting the boat with its full force. Again it landed upright. But there was sudden pressure in the bottom now. "Yeee-e-e—," the Egyptian boatman screamed. "Look!"

Mama's eyes followed the line of his pointing finger to the floor of the boat. A leak—a big one! By the moonlight she could see the water springing up through the hole. "Lord, help us," she cried. Now the boatman was snatching off his clothing and stuffing it into the hole. The water stopped momentarily. But how long could it last?

Mama's eyes searched the dimly lit expanse for a sign of help, but there was no one in sight. She covered her eyes with a wet arm. "Lord," she sobbed desperately, "I need help. I need help. I need help!" But there was only the dark wind to reply. She felt limp, bewildered, felt herself sobbing in her misery. Then she felt a slight bump. Not the jerking of the waves, but a solid something. What could it be? Not land, certainly. She risked leaning to one side and grasped a hard, stalklike object. Then she pulled herself toward it. Cornstalks! A whole pile of them protruding above the water. "Stop," she screamed. "Stop the boat!"

Somehow they managed to clutch the stalks, find some of them imbedded enough to grasp for support, and pull themselves out onto the stalks. Water spewed into the boat wildly now. Seconds later it capsized. But they were safe at least for the moment. Apparently, their cornstalk island was sturdy, perhaps even safe, if the flood waters rose no farther.

But what could cornstalks be doing in such a place? Suddenly Mama remembered. For lack of space the Egyptian fellah usually stacked cornstalks, which he often used for his fuel, high on top of his tiny flat-roofed mud hut. The one-room houses were packed into the villages so closely that there was only a narrow, alleylike road for a passageway around the dwellings. Sometimes the cornstalk piles were twice the height of the huts. This must be the situation under them. Someone must have built his house on too low a level, then had to leave it when the floods came.

Now Mama was most concerned with getting back to dry land, to the donkeys, to the next village, to Jennie, to her children, to Misregee to tell him that now the money was ready for the bricks. A song of joy filled her as she heard the swish of a passing boat. But, though they called and waved, the boat went on in the darkness. Moments later another boat came by. This time the boatman saw them in the revealing moonlight, and stopped.

It was good to get on the donkey's back again, to hear the sound of his quick, sure hooves. How good was the hard board bed in the police station at the next village!

It would be even better to get back home the next morning with the money ready to begin her mighty dream. "Lord, I'm coming home," she smiled to herself, then went to sleep.

Back at home, she began to work earnestly and carefully on the building plans. With ruler, pencil, paper, and a scale for proper proportions she finally got the plans completed. This time she seemed to have it right. And it had taken only a few hours to do it. When she showed it to Misregee, he approved.

The following morning he and Mama staked off the foundation and the boys dug the footing ditches. As soon as they had finished, Misregee began the actual bricklaying for the building. The boys kept the homemade brick forms filled with the mud-manure-straw mix and somehow managed to keep him well supplied with bricks.

When the corner room where Misregee kept his tools was finished, Mama and her children moved into it.

"It's just like Robinson Crusoe," beamed John, her oldest. The English tale was one of his favorites. How many times had she told it, and other classics, to these Egyptian children? She had lost count long ago. She had started making up her own stories now—fables with morals to build her children's lives more completely. And always, of course, she told them stories from the Bible.

Small gifts, but not enough to make their living expenses, came now from the United States, particularly from around the Philadelphia and New York areas where she had talked of her dreams in a number of missions. Also, new Egyptian friends came to her aid. It warmed her heart to realize that Egypt had begun to love her—as she loved Egypt.

Several times at the market Lillian ran into some of the missionaries from the Reverend Dunning's mission house. They were courteous always, but dire in their warnings. She was making a mistake in expanding. She couldn't possibly support all the Egyptian orphans who would descend on her. How would she feed them without any income? Her very life might be endangered. Egyptian authorities would resent her. Something terrible was bound to happen sooner or later.

Lillian always remained cheerful and optimistic in their presence. But she felt a little shaken for a while after their warnings, too. Certainly the missionaries meant well in spite of their pessimism. "Job's comforters," she said silently one day after an encounter. Yet she found herself trembling.

She had occasion to remember their grim prophecy a short time later. It was on a hot summer day, late in the afternoon that she saw a shadow fall across the entrance of their rented home. It was a big shadow, long and haunting. Her eyes moved upward to the man making the shadow. He was rather tall, his features dark and quite handsome, but his clothing was ragged and dirty. His eyes, she saw, were watching the smaller children playing in the yard. Now they focused on one child playing at the side away from the others for the moment. Her eyes followed the line of his vision. It was Fareida he was watching! Suddenly a shaft of fear shot through Lillian. She studied the man's features as he watched the child. Those features were exactly like

Fareida's. Could this be the child's father? Could this be the youth who had come to the Reverend Dunning's mission in the beginning and asked for help? If this were the same man, he had left little Fareida to die, hadn't he? One of the children called Fareida by name and the little girl dashed happily across the yard toward the other child. Now the man was speaking slowly, half mumbling, and getting some official papers from his pocket. All that Lillian could remember later was the man carrying the sobbing little girl away. He would bring her back for a visit some time, he said. She considered getting legal help, but it was no use. No papers had been signed releasing the baby to her in the beginning. She cried for a long time that night, and for many nights afterward. But the worst was yet to come. She received word some time later that Fareida had died.

"How could it have happened?" she cried. "She was in perfect health when I had her?" Then she bowed her head. It was far past her understanding. A part of her died, too, with her firstborn.

Perhaps it was good she had to go on more of her foraging trips to get money for the workmen, as well as for food and supplies for her children. Misregce laid bricks and her boys made them. Mama set out on her donkey staying away all week and returning each Saturday. Windows and doors would cost money. And each worker must be paid his nine piasters per day. How she would get it all only the Lord knew. But she was positive He knew.

When she called on her new friend the mudir again, she found he was willing to help her further. He suggested that when she wanted to go to a village for help she contact his office. He, in turn, would call the village police officer and someone would meet her and take her to the fellahin houses, introducing her to each household throughout the village. "Then they can say something other than 'lady on a donkey,'" he jested gently.

"I don't care what I am called," Lillian answered, laughing, "as long as I get food for my children." She became serious then. "Thank you for the offer," she said. "I would appreciate having someone meet me from the villages."

The mudir's help was manifold. It was a great relief to arrive at a village down the Nile or in the desert fringes and know you were expected. Lillian felt more at ease sleeping in the village jails after it was known that she was an official "guest" in those institutions.

Her arrival became a time of togetherness among villagers—togetherness and happiness. Often she was met by the village police officer himself. He would then take her to the first house in town where she would drink coffee and lukewarm water dipped from the creamy yellow canal waters. She would tell her orphans' story, then go to the next house, telling more about her children. All of the men of each house would then join the group and go on to the other houses. Finally, when they had gone to all of the village houses, all the villagers would be following. At mealtime they would gather at one house and eat. Always Lillian was treated with utmost respect. Yet she longed to get acquainted with the women and girls. But women observed strictly the Arab custom of feminine seclusion, never uttering a word, but serving the best food they could proffer. Often Lillian smiled at them admiringly. Usually the fellah's wife was attractive in a wholesome way, a woman with clear eyes, graceful carriage, usually plump, always quiet, considering herself only as a servant of the home. Once in a while one would almost smile back at Lillian, then abruptly stop herself.

Mama dreamed of becoming close to Egyptian women —so close that she could help them as she longed to do. But that was in the future. In the early 1920's the women of Egypt became Lillian's closest friends. Some of the wealthy women, beautiful in their own distinctive ways, were to become her stanchest supporters and dearest friends, helping her through a half a century. And their children, in turn, would follow in their steps.

A home of their own! The happy days seemed to fly by. They were not rushed by a load of responsibilities as would be the case later. All of the children were close together, working to help one another and the orphanage. The older girls cooked, washed dishes, made clothes, mended, and took care of the babies, under Lillian's close supervision. The boys worked outside, finishing the brick wall, improving the grounds, making chairs and leather goods to sell in the city. Lillian would teach them the English language, which was widely used in Egypt, and read the Bible to them in her room in the evenings. Then would come prayertime, and bed.

But there were more new children who needed a home. They had to enlarge the building with another wing. Then another. Gradually new friends in Egypt helped them more. More than one wealthy Egyptian family became interested and helped with gifts. Still more room had to be made for the weary, ragged little boys and girls who, one, two, three or more at a time, found their way to the orphanage gates. Lillian long ago had vowed never to turn away a needy one. Two or three to one small bed, perhaps. Invent ways to make the food go farther, perhaps. But turn away a needy child? A deserving one? Never!

The seasons were moving along more quickly now. The older boys and girls began to marry and establish their own homes in other places. Lillian was delighted to see that the homes were Christian. New orphans began to come in so rapidly that they were hardly able to build fast enough. She began to take widows who came with their children and begged to stay, too. Earlier, she had taken Oma, a soft-spoken widow and her little boy, and the woman had become such an asset that Lillian wondered how she had ever managed without her.

The year 1917 Lillian counted fifty. Then there were seventy. Then eighty. And still they came. Somehow, Lillian managed to have food and clothing and beds for all of them.

When financial help was plentiful, they ate bountifully; when food was low, they managed as only Lillian could. Jennie proved to be a tremendous help in managing the food supplies. No one could do so much with so little as Lillian's older sister. Not only with food, but in every way, Jennie was most helpful. Always unobtrusive, never demanding, she was loved by everyone, and the little children especially followed her. She would check their ears to be sure they were clean, then would give them a gentle hug and slip them a piece of candy. It was most usual, consequently, to see half a dozen toddlers at Jennie's heels, wanting to have their ears checked because they knew a treat would be ready for them afterward.

Lillian breathed a prayer of thankfulness often for Jennie, so quiet that it was often hard to realize she was present in the orphanage, so understanding in the midst of troubles, so loving to those about her when often love was more desperately needed than any other commodity— even food. Jennie was an earthly saint who asked only one small favor: that Lillian assume the responsibility for financing and running the orphanage. Jennie would fill in, complement her sister's qualities, and quietly love every one around her in the meantime.

A thousand times Lillian wondered where she would find the next day's food for her big Egyptian family. Always it came. Always she prayed without ceasing. Then she mounted her donkey, listened, and went where her Lord seemed to tell her to go.

In the Egyptian villages she nearly always found help. But often there was no proper place for her to sleep. Sleeping on the earthen floors amid rats and fleas was beyond her. So often, she would tug at the cord on the donkey's neck:

"Come my friend," she would tell him. "There wasn't any room for our little Lord Jesus, either. Who are we to complain?" And they would trudge wearily to the police station to spend the night in the jail. If it occurred to her that this was a strange state for a young woman from the depths of America's deep south, she dismissed it from her mind with a swift push. This was her life. Egypt with its multitude of poverty-stricken orphans and widows who needed love and food and shelter as did all God's children.

Gradually, the villagers got to know her, to love her. And when they saw the donkey carrying the American missionary on its back they would wave and say to each other:

"Here comes the lady on the donkey! She has come so far in the desert heat. How tired she looks!"

"How can anyone, except an Egyptian, stand this desert heat?"

"But isn't she really Egyptian now, since she has been one of us so long?"

Those early years became wonderful years. Somehow, she kept going with gifts which she knew came from God: A new denomination, the Assemblies of God, had been formed in 1914, and had become so interested in her work that they often sent barrels of clothing, and when they could the individual members sent money, often at great personal sacrifice. Then, gifts continued to come from Egyptian friends who gradually appeared from the villages and cities and countryside to help. And the little New York Glad Tidings mission never failed to send her an offering of some kind each month.

Always she wrote her benefactors and thanked them graciously, letting them know how much their help had meant and explaining the orphanage needs as she saw them. Additional gifts brought forth additional thanks. Her heart was so full of her children and their needs that it was easy to talk about it and write letters saying "Thank you." Often she sent pictures so people could see what their money was doing. And no matter how big the stack of mail on her desk or how long and hard the day, she disciplined herself to answer each letter personally the same day it was received. Never let a letter go overnight, was her motto. She adhered to it religiously.

How the writers of the letters appreciated this quality! Those who have received Lillian's letters say they had never really been "thanked thoroughly" in their lives until Lillian thanked them for some gift for the orphanage!

By the summer of 1918 there were more than a hundred in the orphanage. That number might have seemed minute later on, but now it seemed huge when food and supplies had to be ready each day for them all on the comparatively meager resources at hand. The future seemed far, far away. The present was the problem. It was all around them, with them at dawn each morning, at the dining tables when it was time for food, and at night when they needed beds. For, by now, Lillian had been able to buy mattresses and beds, not only for her children, but for Jennie and herself. It was good to sleep on a real cotton mattress and springs for a change. Yes, the present was a constant but wonderful problem to Lillian. The future was too far off to consider.

Perhaps it was just as well. A glimpse into the future might have frightened even Lillian's stanch heart.

Chapter IX

ALWAYS SHE saw the eyes. Wherever she went, whatever she did, regardless of how many hours she trudged through the scorching desert heat—she and her donkey—the eyes of Egypt were watching. At the big orphanage she saw the eyes of her children watching her lovingly as she left to search from village to village for the food necessary to feed those who were counting on her. They were beautiful eyes, her children's eyes. Hauntingly beautiful. Mystic. Dark. Heavily fringed with long curving lashes. Smiling eyes, so grateful for their American Mama that their gratitude shone through and embraced her with their glow. Somber eyes, remembering the tragic past before they came into Mama's compassionate outstretched arms. Mama gave them not only love but bread, onions, beans, rice, fresh vegetables—even meat and fruit when she could beg it— and all the time loving them with a love so great that the least child among them could feel it. Ah, those beautiful Egyptian eyes!

Now it was daylight and Mama was about to start on one of her foraging trips. She smoothed her donkey's mane in the stable behind the orphanage, swung herself onto his back, sideways. For an instant she wondered what it would be like to have a saddle so the long hot miles across the desert would be less tiresome, a lovely leather side-saddle. She pushed the beautiful leather saddle resolutely from her mind. She would have a saddle when the Lord was ready for her to have one.

It was July of 1918 now. She rode her donkey silently around the side of the main dormitory. It wasn't time for the children to wake for a few minutes yet. Shortly, Mama knew they would be up, bathing and dressing, each child going to his chore or to his class. This morning was Tuesday, leatherwork school for the older boys, English classes, then sewing lessons for the younger girls, the older girls teaching the younger ones what Mama had taught them.

A soft pecking on the window above her caught her attention. She looked up to see a small face smiling from a second-floor window. Still wearing his white nightgown, a plump little boy was blowing a kiss down to her, tapping on the window with his other hand to get her attention. It was Anwar. Now he was four. She remembered the day he had come as a tiny baby. Less than two pounds, he weighed. So thin and frail he was that she didn't see how he could make it through the first night. So she had wrapped him carefully and taken him to the American Hospital in another section of Assiout. Here the Presbyterian missionary doctors put him in their incubator, the nurses gave him expert care. Perhaps—how she had prayed—perhaps, he might make it after all. She had asked God to care for him, then hurried back to look after the baby's blind mother who was to stay with the other widows at the orphanage. She sighed a little sadly as she remembered his poor mother, and blew him a kiss in return. Anwar's mother had died after a time in spite of all the loving care she had been given.

Mama looked back once more as she rode away. The

window was filled with little faces now, their eyes glowing with a warmth that she knew only love could generate. Nabih, Fouad, Nohad, Sabah, Farid, Said—she could see each pair of eyes smiling, their arms waving joyously. From another wing of the building she saw a group of little girls waving to her. Her eyes, sharp from peering into the endless desert distances, spotted ten-year-old Leila. "Leila, my dear," she said softly, to herself. "How I love you! How I love you!" The little girl had come to her three years before. A diseased foot had to be amputated. Her mother, recently widowed, had wanted to marry again and did not want the crippled child in her way. So she had cast her out. The child had hobbled for miles through desert heat with only a cane to help her. Of course, Mama took her in. Because she was crippled she needed a mother's love even more. This, Mama knew, was in stark contrast to the attitude of most Egyptian mothers. Above all, they loved their children. Their families were bound by the strongest of ties. Poor little Leila's mother was an exception.

Now, she waved once more and turned her face toward the desert. Each of her children had his own pathetic, tragic story. It was best that they all forget the past and live for the future. "Lord, which way?" She closed her eyes, listened.

In a moment they began to move south to a new village where they had never been before. Would they receive Mama and her donkey? Of course they would. The Egyptian mudir would have telephoned the police officer of the village had she asked him. But this morning she had no understanding as to where she was to go. One thing she knew surely, though: She, an American woman must go out today and beg—no, not beg, ask for food for hungry Egyptian children. She asked in the name of her Lord.

The sun was harsh today. It seemed even hotter than the day before when it reached 120 degrees in the shade. The heat burned her skin, seemed to singe her hair, so intense it was, even in the early morning. Her body swayed, jerked, swayed, jerked, following the mechanical donkey rhythm. After a while, her mind dragged away from the desert heat, and went straight back to the "wee ones'" nursery, as she called it fondly. She began to plan a cottage she hoped to have for herself. It would be beautifully shaded from the blasts of the desert sun, with neat rows of fruit trees. Perhaps there would be an acre where she could rest and where the little ones and the older babies and toddlers could play in the fresh air. She passed a hand over her brow wearily. Lately she couldn't tell the difference between going to bed and getting up. She was as tired in the mornings as she was at nights. Perhaps such a cottage would mean getting away from the mighty cares—at least at night. She sighed. Always the tiny nursery was filled with new babies. Gradually, though, she was getting the older girls trained to be little mothers.

Each little girl mother had a family of six babies and it was really remarkable how conscientious they were in their care of their young charges. Formulas had to be fixed, bottles sterilized, cod liver oil given, and the inevitable diapers changed. The tiny ones were sweet to care for. Mama closed her eyes for a moment, daydreaming of what it would be like to have nothing to do but care for the babies in that cottage. Still she was with them a great deal, and always was in charge of them. She thought of how the babies developed from frail, skeletonlike bits of skin, bone, and soul, often suffering with disease, which came to the orphanage, to plump, healthy toddlers. And each one, she realized, had his own individual personality that must develop so that he would not be just another number in a big machine, but a living, wonderful, lovable individual. She thought of the great help the doctors and nurses at the American Presbyterian Hospital had been to her. How could she have managed without them? Mama's newborn babies always were so weak and sickly that they never could have made it without the incubators and expert attention by staff nurses and doctors. That was what they received at the Presbyterian Hospital run by American missionaries. Did it matter that they were Presbyterian missionaries, and that she was not?

How unimportant these things actually were.

She thought again of her early years in Egypt. Perhaps it had been good that progress had been so slow at first. Hadn't she had time to learn to speak the difficult Arabic language those five years? How could she have managed had she had the responsibility that came later with the big increases in numbers? And the babies. Could she have taken care of all the babies in those early days before she had her girls trained to care for them while she was gone. She had been able to train those few children well, when she had only forty or fifty, instead of a hundred. Now, as the older girls took over, they, in turn, trained the young girls in their responsibilities, so that there were always younger girls to take over when the older girls left to marry.

What if she had been given a thousand to care for that first year? Now she knew she had had to grow up with this mighty responsibility herself. How young and impetuous she had been! How could she have lived one day at a time as she now did, not knowing how she would find food for her multitude for the next day? Always, it had been that way. It was certainly good that God knew. One thing she was certain of: From the first, God had supplied her needs. She forced her mind back to her immediate requirements of the day. She was going to a new village in the desert fringes. She must think. Think. Think. Forget the desert heat that was 120 degrees in the shade, and think of important things —such as how to feed a hundred hungry children the next day.

Now it was November 13, 1918. Jennie had left for America. Her rental property in Long Beach, California, had long been needing attention, and when oceanic travel was permitted, she had boarded a ship for her American home.

Mama Lillian had sighed with deep relief the day before when she had heard the armistice had been signed. The war, which Egypt had not wanted and had been drawn into by England, her protectorate, was officially over. But in Egypt the war had left a deep-seated dissatisfaction. The hapless Egyptian fellahin had been seized on the highway and in his fields without warning and sent under escort into service. Each mudir had been required to produce monthly a fixed number of able-bodied men from his province, or answer for the consequences. So, there was bitter resentment. Now with the armistice, the feeling was one of deep discontent. The towns were impatient. The fellahin were dissatisfied. Salaries and wages had not kept up with the cost of living and the workingman and his family were beginning to feel real hunger pangs. To make matters worse, army requisitions had spared the notable and his dependents.

In the midst of this, an arms act was drafted hastily by the English. The act declared that all Egyptians must surrender their weapons to the police. The attempted enforcement of the act brought on a tragic breach between the Egyptians and the British overlords. For in Egypt the respectable householder did not go about defenseless for fear of a calamity.

As the war drew to a close, Egypt was encouraged by President Woodrow Wilson's words to the small nations of the world. The hope that England would give Egypt a measure of independence with the return of peace was a popular subject of conversation in Egyptian homes. And, defying the ruling that forbade public meetings, the Egyptians began to get together and talk behind closed doors of how they could take advantage of the American president's encouragement to the little nations.

Now on November 13, 1918, more drastic news came to the populace. On this day, Saad Zaghlul Pasha, popular revolutionary leader of Egypt, had knocked on the door of the British residency in Cairo. The dashing patriot had been one of three leaders chosen by certain Egyptian men of note to protest the humiliating treatment their country was receiving under English domination.

The theme of their talk that day was independence for Egypt. Concessions, yes—the right of England to occupy the Suez Canal when threatened with attack and to accept English control of the public debt. But independence! There was much unrest, much dickering. Meanwhile the

Egyptians lived under martial law. Finally the patriot Zaghlul and three of his most important adherents were arrested March 8, 1919, and deported to Malta. Egypt was by now filled with seething fury and resentment. Rebellion was inevitable. Then the passionate swelling burst.

Early in March of 1919, history was to begin engraving tragedy in blood and fire on the face of Mama Lillian's beloved Egypt.

In later years she thought of the year as a phantomlike and eerie ghost seen passing in the night. Actually, the year was more dreadful—real, stark, inevitable in a nation as old as time, but new in dreams of independence. For years England had been promising to move out of Egypt. Many felt this was the proper time for the English to withdraw.

Then a shot, fired at a fellah's pigeons, set the nation in motion.

Mama Lillian read about it early one morning in the newspaper. The news account reported that the British had shot six fellahin in front of their families in reprisal for one Englishman who had been pursued by an Egyptian fellah and had died of a heart attack, as a result. It seemed the Englishman was killing some of the fellah's pigeons, and since by law in Egypt, Englishmen could not be tried on any charge, not even murder, the fellah had tried to protect his precious property in the only way he knew. He had pursued the foreigner who could not be brought to justice by court. British authorities had ordered six Egyptian fellahin shot. That, in itself, was rank injustice to the Egyptian populace. What made it doubly tragic was that the six Egyptian men were shot in front of their families. Five of them, it was pointed out, were not connected with the death of the Englishman in any way. It was a reprisal, sixfold.

Mama Lillian could hardly believe the news. Her heart ached for her friends all over this land she had adopted as her own. She heard of the Egyptian rebellion from every side. And she thought of the early beginnings of her own nation. Modern Egypt now compared to her own country in 1776.

She began to hear of more rebellions. They came closer —then arrived with deadly, explosive power in Assiout. Reprisals on the English people who lived in Assiout began in earnest. Reports of British homes being wrecked and burned came to the orphanage. Guns sounded ominously on the Nile barrage near them. The barrage, one of several Nile River dams, had been built with a roadway on top to facilitate travel across the river. Now the open roadway was a carrier of danger to Mama and her orphans.

Days and nights, never free of fear for a moment, began for Mama Trasher. Suddenly fighting men surrounded them, and without further warning there were strangers with knives, clubs, and guns in and out of the orphanage, some even staying there at night. Once, she found herself and her babies and children huddled in an old brick kiln near the orphanage, trying desperately to keep the babies from making a cry which would give them away. She was never to forget that March night of 1919.

In the fearsome darkness, with gunfire sounding in back and from each side of the orphanage, they had gathered the children together, told them briefly to be very calm and quiet, but to hurry as fast as they could to the old brick kiln about three hundred yards in front of the main buildings. The older girls carried the babies and toddlers, one under each arm. Then Mama locked the door and her arms encircled two tiny babies. Their one cow was in the inner courtyard so she was safe unless the house was broken into. Mama shuddered. The whole orphanage was filled with food staples, bedding, valuables of every kind—just what marauders would want. She took her money and her Bible and began to walk with her tiny babies held tightly.

The hot breath of raging fires burned Assiout's night sky. A hay factory had just been set afire, dozens of English homes were in flames on the road between them and the main section of the city, and store buildings were burning. Beautiful Assiout was now only one great flame belching up against the jet-black heavens. Guns resounded across the Nile. Screams pierced the night. Around them, Mama could feel the fighting bearing in now. Stumbling, hurrying breathlessly in the dark, they went silently toward the kiln. Then it happened. Mama felt it before she heard it.

Her heart contracted at the sound of a dull thud behind her. Then there was a sharp cry. She turned. One of the girls had stumbled over something sharp and had dropped a baby girl. The child's eye was bleeding profusely. Mama risked flashing the light on the little face when she felt the blood on it. Quickly she examined the eye, felt on the ground where she had fallen. A gun butt protruded into the air. She felt a large object by the gun—and shrank back when she flashed her light on it an instant. It was a dead British soldier lying across the path, blood still pouring from his disfigured face. She looked once more at the injured baby. "Thank God, it missed her eye," she said, then pressed a handkerchief to the wound. They walked around the dead man and hurried on toward the kiln. Miraculously, the child did not cry.

Safely settled in the old kiln, Lillian's eyes became accustomed to the darkness, and by the moonlight she was able to count heads. Though there were now more than a hundred in the orphanage, Mama Lillian knew every one. Suddenly she gasped. Was it possible? She counted the small heads again quickly and stiffened with fear for an instant, knowing she had another trip to make through the dangerous dark zone. "I'm going back to the babies' dormitory," she told the girl nearest her softly. "There are still two babies back there!"

She heard the girl stifle a cry, then felt her grasp her arm. "Mama, you'll be killed if you go out there now. Look!"

The fighting between the Egyptians and the British had spread to the front of the buildings now. Gunshots rent the darkness with their fury and there were sounds of men scurrying for shelter, fighting with knives, fighting with clubs, then scurrying for shelter. Screams of the injured and dying, shouts of the victors pierced the night air.

But Mama Lillian, her mind on two babies in danger back there in the deserted dormitory, quietly slipped into the night, half hugging the ground as she ran. An eon seemed to pass before she reached the back entrance. Inside she hurried upstairs to the older babies' rooms, and was greatly relieved to find the two toddlers whimpering in the darkness. Whispering comfortingly to them, she hastily grabbed a blanket, covered them and placed them securely in her arms. Then, downstairs. Walking quickly to the main entrance, she huddled there in the dark for eternal minutes. Finally the gunfire seemed to move away to the sides. Then she alternately ran and crawled toward the kiln, praying that the babies she carried would not attract attention by crying.

"Mama has you, babies," she said softly. "You're all right now. God's going to help us get there safely."

Halfway, she hesitated, remembering the dead man and the gun sticking up in the dark path. If she could miss those obstacles she felt sure she could make it the rest of the way. Suddenly, though, she heard shouts behind her, then two shots rang out. She grasped the babies more tightly in terror, and started running. The fighting men couldn't know that she was Mama Trasher carrying two of her Egyptian babies to safety. Not in the jet darkness could they identify anyone, should they want to do so. The shouts burst the night air again. She realized, with certainty now, that they were after her.

Soundlessly, she fell into what seemed to be a ditch, sideways, to keep from hurting her babies. In doing so, she turned her ankle painfully. But she lay there breathlessly praying in silence. Minutes later she realized that she had fallen into a slight depression and was lying beside the dead British soldier. It was the safest place they could have fallen. The dead body formed the only protection they had. She hardly noticed the severe pain that flashed wildly from her right ankle to her hip. The ankle began to throb mercilessly, but there was no time to think about it. One of the babies whimpered, the other answered.

"Sh-h-h-h—" said Mama Lillian. "God loves you, dears. Be very quiet and Mama will sing to you." Then ever so softly, in whispered tones, she began to sing as the searching steps crushed and crackled the dry earth around them.

Closer and closer they sounded until she could almost feel them walking on her. Then, a foot stepped on her shoulder. She cringed in pain from the weight but didn't make a sound. Evidently the owner of the foot thought she was the dead soldier in the darkness. The foot lifted, moved. A volley of shots sounded from the south and the searching steps scurried away. Now one of the babies whimpered again.

"Sh-h-h—" said Mama. "Jesus loves me, this I know," she sang almost soundlessly, praying as she did so that it would quiet the frightened baby. "For the Bible tells me so." Suddenly a bullet whined above, exploded with a blast close to her face, the dust choking her. With her free hand she brushed the dirt from her face. "Little ones to Him belong. They are weak but He is strong. . . ."

The shots faded away finally. The dark night air was quiet. Was this the time to run? "Lord, is it?" She listened for an answer. She found it in another silent moment about her. Quickly she got a firm hold on her two babies, at the same time whispering a prayer for help and guidance— and ran. Finally, breathing in hard gasps, she crept inside the old brick kiln and sank to the earthern floor. She uncovered the babies in her arms, hugged them gently before handing them to older girls.

"Mama," a soft voice said, "we've been praying that you would make it back alive." The girlish voice broke. "If anything had happened to you—"

"Yes, Mama," another girl's voice said softly. "We couldn't live without you."

"Sh-h-h-h-h-h—" Mama whispered. "Each one try to get your babies to sleep. It's our only chance—to keep everything quiet." Then, rubbing her ankle to keep down the pain, and trying to shut from her hearing the constant sounds of gunfire and from her vision the exploding fires which ballooned grotesquely into the dark sky above her beloved Assiout, she began to repeat the comforting words of the Ninety-first Psalm which she had said many times at evening prayers.

"A thousand shall fall at thy side and ten thousand at thy right hand; but it shall not come nigh thee.

"Only with thine eyes shalt thou behold and see the reward of the wicked.

"Because thou hast made the Lord, which is my refuge, even the most High thy habitation,

"There shall no evil befall thee, neither shall any plague come nigh thy dwelling."

When she had finished she asked Edward, one of the older boys, to repeat it in Arabic. Mama was too exhausted to say more.

At daylight she felt it was safe for her to slip outside. Quiet had settled. Fires still raged in Assiout and in the neighborhood, but the fires were fast turning to ugly black smoke that moved aimlessly across the charred ruins like an aftermath of a hideous nightmare. Mama walked swiftly to the orphanage, unlocked, then went back for her children and babies. All seemed to be well for the moment. At least they could prepare a good breakfast and give the babies their milk.

That night it seemed safe to stay in the orphanage. At least there was no fighting going on around them. The girls went upstairs to put the babies to bed, the boys were at work in their dormitory. Mama was alone in the parlor when she heard a loud knocking on the front door.

She answered, thinking someone needed help, as had been the case so many thousands of times when a similar knock had sounded. When she opened the door she stifled a scream of fear. Facing her were hard-faced, fierce-appearing men, armed with long knives and clubs. Now they were pressing toward, against her, until she felt she was suffocating. She fell back, realizing as she saw the men coming closer that she was all alone in this part of the orphanage, as the older girls were upstairs with the babies and the older boys were studying in their rooms.

Suddenly a new face appeared in the crowd. She started to cry out a warning when she saw it was her neighbor, Said. But she thought better of it. Now he pushed his way to her, then moved directly in front of her, facing the intruders, and threw his arms high.

"Men of Araby," he cried to them. "What are you doing? This American lady has given her life to taking care of our widows and orphans—our own Egyptians. Would you destroy all of this?" In answer, the ruffians moved in closer. Mama Trasher saw their knives flash in the light. Looking at them, she knew they must be from some faraway part of the country, that she was completely unknown to them. The largest one, their leader, moved forward. His unruly black beard smelled of sweat and his eyes were red and angry. "If you do not move you will be killed." His eyes were on Said. Like one of their knives in sharp movement, the eyes seemed to pierce him. Now his knife blade was pressed against Said's stomach. But Said refused to budge. Though much smaller than the ruffians, and unarmed, he stood straight and faced them doggedly.

"Lord, help us," Mama prayed silently.

Someone was moving behind them now. The big man suddenly drew his knife away from Said, motioned to the others, and they walked into the darkness as quickly as they had come.

Mama turned to thank Said. But he was gone too—back to his little house across the field.

Trembling, she closed the door, went upstairs to her rooms. "Is something wrong, Lord?" she asked silently. She knelt by her bed and listened.

Near the end of March, 1919, the situation became so desperate that British authorities ordered all foreigners to leave for their "own protection."

"But I am not a foreigner," Mama protested. "I belong in Egypt just as my Egyptian friends belong here. And what would my big family of orphans and widows do without me?"

"Sorry, madam, but we have our orders," an efficient voice clipped out at her door one morning. Then more gently: "You can go to see the general at the British Embassy in the morning. But his answer will be the same."

Downhearted, dispirited, she left the general's office the following morning. His answer had been the same. There was nothing left.

"Is this what you want me to do, Lord?" She had spent the night at the American Embassy, with all her children sleeping there or at the American hospital. All night she had heard their muffled sobs. When they should have been sleeping they were crying. But leaving seemed the only thing to do, though she thought her heart would burst within her when the realization finally came to her in full. All night she had cried for help, for strength, for knowledge. To leave her children after nine years of backbreaking, discouraging work when all seemed to be progressing so well now was almost too much. What would her children do? She stared at the twinkling Egyptian sky, the peaceful full moon, then closed her eyes. "What am I supposed to do, Lord?" she asked.

At daylight she knew the answer. Once more she felt peace abiding within her. She would have Oma, one of her most competent and loyal Egyptian widows and Mr. Nashid, her faithful Egyptian assistant, take charge of the orphanage and would send them operating money back from America. Then, when God said so, Mama would return to her beloved adopted land.

The British ships, the *Victoria* and the *Puritan*, were waiting on the Nile to take all foreigners out the next morning. Calmly, slowly, hugging her precious blue wool cape around her shoulders, Mama boarded the *Puritan* with only her worn brown grip as her luggage, then turned to say goodbye. She would never forget this moment that she turned to the shore. A hundred pair of her children's beautiful eyes were on her. She could feel the glow of their devotion coming through to her across the water as the ship pulled out and began its trip down the Nile to Cairo. Some of them, mostly the little ones, were crying, calling for her. The older ones just watched her quietly and waved, their solemn dark eyes telling her to hurry home to them. She knew, from conversations she had overheard, that they had agreed not to cry if they could help it, because "it would make Mama feel even worse." As long as she could see them from the deck of the Nile steamer they were waving, blowing their kisses and watching her with eyes she thought were the most beautiful eyes in the world.

That was March 27, 1919. She vowed as she left them to return when the time was ripe. Now tears she had held back broke the barrier of reserve she had held in front of her children. She leaned her head on the rail of the ship and sobbed until she was completely spent. Whatever happened to her, nothing could be so sorrowful as this parting. Egypt was her whole life. To Egypt she had given her whole love. "Egypt, Egypt, how I love you!" she sobbed quietly as Assiout faded and the steamer slid through the Nile waters.

Back in the United States she felt almost a stranger— indeed, she felt a foreigner in her own native country. She stopped in New York City, then made several stops in other cities before she went on to Jennie's home in Long Beach, California. Everywhere she was invited to talk about the Assiout orphanage and everywhere she was given money generously. People wanted to help once they knew the need. She was deeply impressed by the people of the new denomination, the Assemblies of God, in whose churches she was welcomed with open arms. She felt the need now to belong, to feel that a praying group of Christians were her own people. Of course, she knew this young denomination could not begin to support her big enterprise in Egypt. But the fervor of these Pentecostal people who had founded the Church in 1914 was so closely akin to the fervor within her own heart that she was glad to become one of their members. Very quickly they showed their willingness to give to her cause individually. And though the people were not generally monied, they were more than generous with what they had. Most important to Mama Lillian were their earnest prayers for her. Their prayers were like hers—warm, direct, sincere, and constant. When she joined, she felt complete in a quiet, calm, and warm glow.

But even though she was in the United States, with none of the problems of the orphanage pressing upon her, she had no time to think of her own needs. In fact, she was surprised to find she *had* almost no personal needs. A change of work dresses, a dark dress for church, her precious blue cape for cold evenings, a beautiful pair of leather shoes made by her older boys—she had these. What more could she want? What more could any woman need? She couldn't wear but one dress and one pair of shoes at a time.

She was staying at Jennie's Long Beach home when she finally went to town to do some personal shopping one summer day in 1919. Walking briskly along the street in her good homemade shoes, she noticed the windows for the first time. Dresses for women—how short and boxy were the styles with the waists lowered almost to the hips. How ugly they were compared to the long flowing black robes she remembered the graceful Egyptian women wearing. She passed a restaurant. There behind the window were several large pies. Mama Lillian paused. Ah, homemade pie. She drew closer. There was an apple pie, and over there was a peach pie and—oh, lemon meringue! Fluffy meringue piled high. Flaky crust. How often had she longed for pie during those nine lean years at the Assiout orphanage! But

all she could look forward to was besara or rice or beans.
Besara! She disliked the cereal food profoundly. Yet she
had eaten it for nine years, as she had eaten rice and beans,
onions, bread. Whatever the others had had, that had been
her fare, too. But now—

She opened the door of the restaurant, smiled in anticipation, her mouth watering. She sat down at a clean, white-
clothed table. The waitress stood by her now. "May I have
your order?" she said. Mama looked up, a little surprised,
and started to answer. But without any warning the muscles
of her throat contracted. She felt herself choking. She
gasped hoarsely, tried to apologize. Quickly she rose and
hurried outside, her eyes filled with tears which stung like
a thousand fires in the desert. Not looking to the right or
left, she hurried to Jennie's home, washed her burning eyes
with cool water, sat down at her desk with her diary. From
all directions she could feel the eyes, the beautiful, haunting, mystic eyes of Egypt. Her children's eyes, and their
arms, reaching across the world to her. "Egypt, Egypt, how
I love you!" she whispered earnestly.

"I couldn't eat your pie," she wrote. "It belongs to you—
in Egypt."

Chapter X

MAMA'S RETURN to Egypt in the spring of 1920 was a triumphant one even though it didn't seem so at the time. A few of her children had gone, and supplies such as blankets and clothing had dwindled nearly to nothing. But Oma and Mr. Nashid, her faithful Egyptian helper, had managed their parts well and had taken good care of the children, especially the babies. Mama was greatly encouraged, too, to find a barrel of clothing and several packages from her new friends in America. She realized, of course, that the young denomination had not assumed the responsibility of her big Egyptian orphanage, but the realization that she was not alone in human support gave her a warm, vibrant feeling and renewed courage. For her part, she wanted to continue to operate her orphanage on faith. It was the way God intended it. But she deeply appreciated the Assemblies of God people and their earnest desire to help. These devout, praying Christians were to form a strong chain of faith for Mama through the years.

Now she began to gather up the loose ends on all sides. She looked up old Egyptian friends who had helped them in the past and her friendly, warm personality was enhanced by the new zest she now had and the encouragement of her new church friends in the United States. New children now began making their way to the orphanage in such numbers that it seemed as if she could gaze at the far

153

desert horizon and see the long line she had visualized at the first. Only now the line was real. Perhaps the leaner years during and after World War I had caused the circumstances which now brought such increased numbers to the big front gates. By 1926 there were more than five hundred. Then, on September 10, 1926, a new light came into Mama's life. For indeed, the little girl who knocked at the gates that day proved to be a veritable ray of light for years to come.

Little Lateefa Bishay was seven years old, soft-spoken, affectionate, intelligent—and blind.

Yet Mama was to find that Lateefa could see when those around her who saw with their eyes could not. Eventually, she would become a trusted English and Braille teacher in the orphanage. But in September, 1926, she was only the first of the blind girls that became a long procession of the sightless into the orphanage. Of all Mama's children, they were especially sensitive and responsive to her love and care. It is so dark when you are blind in Egypt, she thought sadly and often. She smiled when she remembered the evening her "seeing" girls had come to her with their problem. They wanted to have a private time of Bible reading in the courtyard before they went to bed.

"But Mama," they explained, "we can't see because it is too dark when we're finished with our work."

A few nights later the problem was solved. Mama saw the group of older girls sitting in the moonlight, heard someone reading distinctly from the Bible though it was dark. She walked closer, stared in astonishment. Blind Lateefa, feeling the symbols in her Braille Bible, was reading to them in her beautiful clear voice. She could read when the others could not see in the darkness!

There was hope for blind boys in Egypt through the government school for blind boys. But nowhere was there a place for blind girls in that country. Nowhere except with Mama. She was deeply touched by the amount of blindness throughout Egypt. Most of the trouble, she knew, was caused by the millions of flies in the land. The filthy flies were everywhere. In sewage, drainage ditches, in drinking water, on the food, on the bodies of the people, and eternally on and around their eyes in great clusters causing disease which led to blindness. Without screens on the windows and doors, with no present-day disinfectants for use against the insects, what chance did the poor Egyptians have?

Mama was even more careful now to teach her children proper sanitation and the great numbers of children now coming to the orphanage made it necessary to begin new buildings to improve conditions, as well as to make more room. As usual, she began each building with but a few piasters, her now well-known "three bricks ahead," and a fervent prayer for help. Then, as in the past, she got on a donkey (she had now acquired her own) and went out to seek help. As in the past, she asked Divine guidance. "Which way, Lord? I'm listening."

But a new day was coming for Mama. It came on wheels. If she could have foreseen it she would have been exuberantly happy, though for the moment she would have been saddened by the drastic change which was to strike her life. She was sitting in the luxurious drawing room of a wealthy Egyptian home when chagrin and shame overcame her. She had come here early this morning so desperate had been her need for money for flour, kerosene for cooking, soap, and other supplies. She also was badly in need of money to pay the laborers for laying bricks for another new building.

Money was needed immediately to pay the teachers. Two of her older boys needed money to take government examinations. She was more desperate today than usual, so great were the needs of her children. But she had been told the man of the house was not yet up when she had come early this morning. When she returned at noon, servants told her he had gone out. When she returned in the afternoon, he was in but could not see her at present, the servants said.

"Thank you," Mama said firmly. "I'll wait." So a woman servant had seated her in the drawing room, and for a long moment stood looking at Mama. Finally, she shook her head sadly. "If I had money, I would give you what you need myself." Then she turned and hurried out in tears. When she had gone Mama realized to the fullest that she was not wanted in this house. A great wave of loneliness and tiredness swept over her. Finally she began to weep bitterly. She felt her spirit was broken, that she could not go on.

"I can't do this any more, Lord," she sobbed quietly. "I simply can't!" She sobbed quietly for several minutes, then quickly knelt beside her chair. "I'll take care of the children, Lord. You provide the money. I can't go out on my donkey any more and beg. I can't do it and have the strength to care for my children." She stopped then. Even now it seemed incredible to her that the numbers had swelled so greatly. Why, only this week forty new ones had been accepted. She recalled the missionary's words of discouragement when she was beginning the first orphanage building. "They'll descend on you in droves," she'd said. To Mama, their coming in such great numbers was a miracle, a wondrous welcome miracle. And she welcomed each diseased,

starving infant, each blind girl, each tired widow, each
ragged, hungry child with open arms, her heart filled with
love for every one. Still, those hundreds of newcomers were
the cause of the urgent new needs for food and supplies
she seemed unable to cope with of late. Now she said,
calmly and quietly: "Lord, will you please send me seventy-
five pounds? Today? Then I'll know that You are in agree-
ment, that I am following Your Will." Then she arose
and left the wealthy Egyptian's house.

At the orphanage she found that an Egyptian friend had
been there in her absence. Oma smilingly handed her a
container with the friend's note enclosed. His daughter
had become engaged, the message read, and the family
wanted to share their happiness with Mama. When she
looked in the box she found not seventy-five pounds but
two hundred pounds.

She heaved a deep sigh and closed her eyes. "Thank
You, Lord," she whispered. "Now I know. Now I know.
I've made my last begging trip on my donkey. Now I know
for sure!"

A short time later, in October, Mama's well-to-do Egyptian women friends pooled their finances and presented
her with a new car. When Mama learned to drive it she
was able to bring in supplies and to carry on Orphanage
business far more efficiently than in the past. It was certainly no longer necessary for her to ride her donkey through
the desert heat and to endure physical hardships beyond
her strength. She still operated her orphanage on a "hand-
to-mouth" basis—"from God's hand to Lillian's mouth,"
she said often. Times were still hard, yes. But times were
wonderful.

On October 11, 1927, she wrote in her diary: "A very

poor woman came to us today. She is ill and blind and expecting a baby. She has three other children, and her husband has been out of work for eight months. The children have absolutely nothing to eat. She walked all the way to the orphanage, about four miles. We are nearly out of money ourselves, but I thought that poor Toffa was in a worse condition than the orphanage, so I gave her five dollars, a dozen loaves of bread, some rice, sugar, and six bars of soap. Then I took her to town in the car and bought her some tomatoes, potatoes, cooking butter, and several pounds of meat. I told her she could come and stay with us after she was confined.

"Faheema said that we needed some rice and sugar, so after I took Toffa home I went to Badeer's grocery to buy them. One of the clerks asked me if I wanted to buy a large sack of the best rice. I told him that I wanted only a basket of the medium-grade rice and a box of sugar. Mr. Badeer came out and told the man to get me the sack of good rice, a big box of sugar, and one hundred pounds of soap. I said, 'No, I cannot buy so much rice, and I really don't need any soap today.' He said, 'Take it and keep it until you do need it.' He filled my car with boxes of bluing, buttons, etc., and I had to send Habib with the donkey cart to bring the rice and other things!

"In the evening Dr. Aziz came and brought me fifty dollars which Mr. Albert Khyat had given him to give as a thank offering. He had just become engaged. Dr. A. also gave five dollars of his own money.

"We gave Toffa five dollars and God sent us fifty-five. We gave her a few pounds of rice; God gave us a whole sack, worth about twelve dollars. We gave the poor woman six bars of soap and we were given one hundred pounds. She received a few pounds of sugar and we a whole box full. Mr. Badeer had never given us anything before."

On November 9: "Hallen Wessa has become engaged today. . . . to Leon and has sent me an invitation to the reception. Her mother enclosed a check for two hundred fifty dollars, so I paid all my debts. The American mail on Monday also brought us one hundred dollars, 'Your Heavenly Father knoweth that ye have need of all these things.' "

November 12: "All of our money gone again. I borrowed twenty dollars from Faheema, eight dollars and fifty cents from Fardnse, and one dollar from Bobbie to pay the workmen. We haven't a cent."

November 17: "Busy all day making uniforms for the family. I hear from Cairo that all of Thomas Cook's Nile tourists are booked to come to the orphanage. I am trying to finish the uniforms so the children will look well."

November 19: "This is a busy day. We are trying to have everything nice as we are expecting the tourists between four and five. I am tired. I do hope they will give me something for the children. . . . The tourists all came, crowds and crowds of them. Some came in; others stayed out in front in their carriages. Our little boys gave out pamphlets about the orphanage, and the whole family of children went out to see the people. They did look so sweet. I was proud of them. All who went up to the Nursery were greatly touched as they saw the rows of tiny beds and wee babies in them, some with their bottles and others sitting on the carpet playing.

"While I was showing the tourists around a rather poor-looking old Egyptian walked down toward the main building. I stopped and spoke to him, asking him to come in. He said, 'No, not now.' Some of the tourists handed Miss Ryott thirteen dollars for the orphanage. After everyone left I saw the old man walking along and so again asked him to come in. As he entered the drawing room he handed me a bill. It was fifty dollars. I nearly laughed out loud. It was such a good lesson to me. I had been working all week to fix up the children and the place for the rich tourists and they gave me thirteen dollars, and a poor old Egyptian whom one scarcely notices, hands me a fifty-dollar bill! 'God's ways are not our ways.'

"I went to the post office and found thirty-three dollars from America in the different letters. We cut out clothes until midnight. Stopped because it was Sunday morning. It is rather wonderful the way God gives us strength to go from day to day. The boys are doing wonderful work preaching the Gospel in the different villages every Sunday. The crowds are growing all the time. I am glad they are so interested in village work."

November 20: "I went over to see Mrs. Nasif Wessa and stayed for dinner. Habib Bey Doss, Mr. Albert Khyat, Amin Bey, and others were there. Habib Bey told us that the Coptic Bishop, who is a millionaire, is having trouble, as the government is making some investigation as to what he is doing with all of the church money. He thought the best thing to do would be to give some to the poor every year. So he went to Cairo and got a lawyer to make out legal papers specifying different charities and the amount each was to receive each year. He decided to give our orphanage one thousand dollars a year, but the lawyer, in writing it out, got confused because there were so many items, and put us down for one hundred twenty-five dollars instead. The Bishop noticed it, but did not think it worth while to change it.

"Habib Bey asked me if it was not time for me to put a limit to the number of children I would accept in the orphanage. I told him that it was almost impossible for me not to take in new children as people kept dying and leaving orphans. 'Well, you will have to stop sometime,' he said. 'Yes,' I said, 'when God stops sending in enough money to support them, I'll stop taking in new ones.'

"While I was there at Mrs. Wessa's my secretary telephoned saying that Dr. Zackie had just brought up two sheep for the children's supper. . . . When I reached home the girl in charge of the nursery came and said that the two sheep were not enough for the children, and that there was not enough meat to make any soup for the babies. I said, 'Go to the orphanage kitchen and tell the cook to give you some for the nursery.' She came back and said there was none left. Then I told her to cook some rice.

"I went out and sat on the bridge in front of my house. It was dark, but a car drove up and stopped. I heard a man say, 'Well, don't stay long.' Another said, 'You help me lift it from this side.' I said to one of the girls who was sitting with me, 'That sounds as though we are getting something.' I arose and went out to meet the man. Though it was quite dark, I saw two men carrying in half a beef. As they put it down on one of the tables, one of the little girls said, 'I told the babies to pray for God to send them some meat.' I called Malazama and said, 'Go light the stove and cook the meat. The babies can have soup for breakfast tomorrow!' "

November 21: "American mail brought in about one

hundred seventy-five dollars. I went to town and spent over one hundred dollars for food, blankets, cloth, and bedding. It is now nearly midnight. We can say with grateful hearts, 'Hitherto hath the Lord helped us.' "

November 22: "I started writing at sunrise, had breakfast, dinner, and supper at my writing desk; stopped only long enough to go and see Mr. F. on business.

November 26: "I bought forty dollars' worth of cloth today and we have only twenty-five dollars left. The girls are cold as winter has started and I have not been able to buy any winter clothes yet. Yesterday we took all that we had out of the storeroom and gave them to some girls; it was awful to have to push dozens and dozens of them away and tell them that there was nothing left, while they were all calling out: 'Wa ana ya, Mama.' ('And I, Mama')."

November 28: "American mail brought forty dollars and three packages of clothing."

November 29: "Mrs. H. brought me a new baby; it is ill and may not live."

November 30: "We are all out of money again. Mrs. Nasif Wessa just telephoned to say she was sending fifty ardebs of wheat (enough to last us five weeks and worth about four hundred dollars). American mail brought eight dollars."

December 1: "I went to town three times. Oma Amin sent three bolts of cloth for the boys. Twenty-five dollars came in. Mr. Nashid is ill; his temperature is 103 degrees. (He is my head worker and bookkeeper; also married one of my girls.)"

December 2: "We started burning bricks today for the new girls' building."

December 3: "I haven't a cent. I feel ill, but I cannot go to bed as Mr. Nashid is sick and I have to see about the boys carrying the bricks. Oh, it is awful to be ill and not have enough money and so many needs. I went to the post office to see if any money had come. There was a letter asking me to take a poor widow and her child."

December 7: "Edna Wessa sent me one hundred dollars and Faheem Effendy sent twenty-five. I paid Hanna Effendy one hundred dollars to pay the bill for the paint and nails. I just got the money all safely spent and in comes one of the big boys saying that seven boys who are taking the government school examination must have ten dollars each at once! Well, I didn't have any, so I went to Assiout to see what I could do. I soon had ninety dollars given me so I gave the boys the seventy and had a little left over."

December 15: "Mrs. Wessa gave me one hundred twenty dollars. I bought cloth for the women's underwear and cloth to make coats for the children. There is not a cent left in the house."

December 24: "The Lord has supplied us with a lovely Christmas. We had a fine time with the children. We made bags and filled them with nuts and candy. Oh, how the children enjoyed them! We gave out the toys last week; everyone got something nice. The women all got under-clothes. Oh, I was tired when it was all over, but the children had made me so many nice Christmas presents that I forgot how tired I was."

December 25: "I had Christmas dinner with Mrs. N. Wessa."

In 1928, Mama wrote:

January 5: "Mrs. Nasif took me to Cario with her for a

few days as her sister was not well after the birth of her baby."

January 10: "I left Cairo today. Wadeah (the lady who was ill) is doing fine. She gave me one hundred dollars and her husband gave me another hundred. The baby's grandmother gave me twenty-five dollars and its other grandmother gave fifty ardebs of wheat (worth about four hundred dollars) and Camille Sanad sent me fifty dollars, Quite a lot came in from America, so we are once more comfortable."

January 31: "We got three newborn babies this month; their mothers died when they were born—Amena, Obgy, and Marium."

February 13: "We have only seven dollars today. Oh, I am so tired. We have had company all morning. Everybody wants to see the whole place and it keeps me climbing stairs all day long. I get so tired saying the same things over to everybody. I sometimes feel that I could take people around in my sleep and say the right thing at the right time! 'There are the widows' rooms. No, the babies are in the other building— No we don't send the girls out as servants— Now just come this way and I will show you the little boys' rooms; yes, we make all of our own bricks; yes, those are our own cows; no, we don't own all of that land, the owner won't sell; etc., etc.' People's brains all seem to work in the same way, because they all seem to ask nearly the same questions. Oh, it is lovely of them to be so interested and I love to show them around, but oh, I am so tired!"

February 14: "Katy left today to be married; how I shall miss her. The telephone company telephoned that they wanted thirty dollars for the year's subscription. I said,

'All right, I will send you the money at once.' I only had twelve dollars and fifty cents. I started out to pay the man! I visited a girl friend first and one of her cousins was there for tea. He said, 'Lillian, why don't you go get the money out of the charity box at the Nile Club. I lifted it the other day and it seemed quite heavy.' I went at once and I found sixty-two dollars and sixty cents in it. I, of course, went and paid the telephone bill as I had promised to do."

February 17: "I went and preached at the big boys' orphanage [which was near Mama's main building]. There was such a sweet spirit of interest among them and they are doing such good work in the villages."

February 18: "We have only twelve dollars and that will not be enough to pay the workmen. . . ."

February 23: "Mr. Doss Gholter died today and his family had two calves killed at the gate as his body was taken out, for the good of his soul. They sent the meat to us. We have had meat three times this week."

In 1930 she recorded:

Thanksgiving Day: "Many times God not only sends help, but sends the very thing we are in need of. Two weeks ago, the woman who has charge of the little boys' nursery, came to me saying that the children's mattresses were torn and so badly worn through that some of them were nearly sleeping on the springs. I told her that I was very, very sorry, but I had no money at all and that I thought all last year's cotton was used up. I told her that they would have to pray for God to send help. I sent for the woman in charge of bedding. As we were all three talking about it, and as she was telling them that there was not a bit of cotton left from last year, I looked out of the window, and saw a large motor truck drive up, piled with huge sacks of cotton (worth about fifty dollars), a gift to the orphanage.

"Three days later, some of the girls came to the woman in charge of the soap asking for their allowance. She said, 'We have none.' . . . The same day . . . this woman's mother, who was ill, had sent for some rice. The storeroom supply was down to only a few handfuls.

"About five o'clock a car drove up with all kinds of gifts piled in it, large and small. There were six large five-gallon tins of butter, six tins of cheese, a large sack of soap, a sack of rice, two and a half boxes of sugar, and many smaller things, worth perhaps over one hundred dollars in all. A woman had died four months previous, and before her death, she had asked her relatives to please send the things in her storeroom to the orphanage."

Friday: "We are six hundred dollars behind; it is the last of the month and tomorrow we will have to pay three hundred in salaries to our teachers and workers. The American mail came bringing four dollars. The man from whom we had been buying our bread said that he will not let us have any bread tomorrow, as we owe him one hundred fifty dollars. He is a poor man and needs the money. Hundreds of children and widows are looking to me for food. . . .

"Sunday before last I went to visit one of my Egyptian friends who is ill. I spent the day with her and she asked me how many children I had. I told her and she asked me how much money I had. I told her that I had less than five dollars and that I had borrowed two hundred fifty dollars from one of my friends. She then inquired about our new buildings saying, 'Of course you don't start a building until you have some extra money on hand.' I said, 'Oh, we do not wait for money. When we are quite sure that we need the new building, we start if only with fifty cents, and by the time the building is finished, it is also paid for.' I told her of our large two-story building, which we built last year for the girls—how we did not owe a cent on it. After I had been talking a long time, telling her how God met the needs, she said: 'Well, Lillian, if I didn't know it was true, I'd say it was all lies!' As I left that evening her husband gave me twenty-five dollars. The next morning fifty-five dollars came from America. I paid back part of the two hundred fifty dollars which I owed."

On October 2, 1932, Mama wrote: "Never have I seen such days. . . . These days are ones of great testing and, at the same time, days of wonderful blessing. Never before has He been so near and never before have I felt His presence so real.

"Should I go to town or not; should I go down this street or the other; should I write a certain letter or not? 'The steps of a good man are ordered by the Lord.' If He orders our steps, how very careful we should be that they take us only where He has ordered. . . . He has promised to lead us.

"One day last month we decided to have special prayer that the needs would be met. . . . Afternoon came and we did not have a cent. There was no breakfast food and no bread for tomorrow. (We have to have the flour the day before we need the bread because we bake at night.) I got in my car and drove to town and went from place to place, but I found that either people were out or they had never thought about giving any money to the orphanage. Dark came on, but I was not able to get one cent."

Mama laid her pen on the desk then and walked to the window that overlooked the Nile. Her memory filtered back through the days. . . .

She had braked the car that night, bowed her head to the wheel. Tears coursed down her cheeks. Would tomorrow be the day when her children had no bread? Was their prayer heard? What would the children believe if no help came? That their prayers had failed? That God had failed?

"Oh, no, no!" Mama cried. "Children, God will *never* fail!" She stared at the dirt road in front of her. She couldn't think of another place to go.

That evening she met Mr. Nashid, one of her Egyptian workers. Together, they drove to a house where they had not let Mama in previously. She felt she had to try once more. After that there was nothing more she could do.

She knocked, smiled when the door opened. When she left she had a small amount, enough for breakfast food and the kerosene to cook it with, and a little more. But nothing for bread.

They then went to a man who owed them money, but he told them to come the first of the month. "Where shall I drive you?" Mr. Nashid asked. "The Lord will have to direct me, for I know of no other place in town," said Lillian.

"Mama," he said. "Mr. Berlin has not yet given us the flour which he gives us every year."

"Of course!" She had quite forgotten this. They drove to his home and asked him for the flour.

He was very willing to help. There were ten sacks— enough to last about four days.

Mama returned to her desk, began to write again:

"There are no words which can express my joy," she wrote. "God was faithful. . . ."

"Each day we have to trust Him for every single thing that is needed in the home. 'Your Heavenly Father knoweth that ye have need of all these things.' "

On November 3, 1932, she wrote her friends in America: "I thank God that we are getting along all right, day by day; but we are not able to keep up the salaries (which are about two hundred dollars a month). We have sent away all of the workers that we can get along without; so there is no possible way of cutting it down any lower. . . .

"We have started some new sewing classes. All the little girls are now being taught how to make the clothes for both the boys and the girls. They are so delighted when they finish their pieces. I get such pleasure watching them. I have a large tree in front of my rooms and I put a rocking chair and table out in the garden and let the little girls each take a jacket and work on it. The older girls help me, although I enjoy doing it myself. Sometimes I have other things to do and cannot attend to it myself every day; then the older girls do it. As I write this, they are all busy making little jackets for the baby boys. They make very nice quilts also."

January 5, 1933: "I realize that these are the days and this is the time that the Lord would have us 'stand still and know that I am God.' Also the Word tells us, 'If thou faint in the day of adversity, thy strength is small.'

"It is not only a lesson to me and to the children, but all of the people of Assiout are watching with wonder to see how the orphans are being fed and cared for while others are in such great need. Not only are they looking on and wondering; they are all trying to help with whatever little gift they are able to give. The schools here have been showing a lovely spirit. They get the girls of each class to come out and visit the orphanage; each one bringing some rice, sugar, oranges, cloth, or money. The missionaries have also shown a very great spirit of love and sacrifice toward us, especially the Presbyterians. Many of them have helped us this year by sending money and clothes. This has been a very hard year for them also; so it makes us appreciate their gifts so much more.

"We have bought three new bicycles for the older boys to use in the villages where there are no churches. One of the boys who is nineteen years old is in charge of the village work (consisting of preaching services and Sunday schools). He is a nice boy, and I believe he will be a great blessing to these dear people.

"We have not been able to get nearly enough winter clothes for the children, but it is really wonderful how the Lord seems to keep them well. In church we seldom hear a cough. . . ."

March 13, 1933: "Some one brought us tiny twin babies this morning. Poor little things. Their mother died when they were born. . . . I am afraid they will not live. Anyway we will do our best. We have eight tiny babies, some a few days old. Then of course we have dozens of middle-size babies; some just learning to walk, and others known as the 'big babies.' "

April 27, 1933: "Sometimes I get so tired that I feel I cannot stand another thing; then I ask Him to give me a rest for a few days and to please send in the money on time, so as to save me the strain. These are what I call my 'rest' days. There come days and weeks when it seems as if every cent comes by force, and not until I have been tested to the uttermost does my 'rest' come. But it always comes!"

One day in early summer, 1933, Mama went to a village where she had never been before. One of the boys had been going there to preach and wanted to open a school and mission. The village, called Sheik Soufi, was on the edge of the desert.

They found the four walls of a church with a sort of roof that had been made of cornstalks with a few beams to hold them up.

"To whom does this church belong?" she asked. The people shook their heads. A long time ago, they said, a rich man deeded it as a church. But the man had died years ago. They had no preacher now.

They had had a preacher once—a student from the American Presbyterian College who came every Sunday morning. But they had had to withdraw him. They had agreed to pay him about five piasters each Sunday to pay for the donkey on which he came. But finally they were not able to pay it. That was seventeen years ago.

Prayerfully, in her diary Mama wrote: "We hope to put a new top on the old church and open a school and mission there this summer. How we hope the little boys and girls of today will get what their fathers lost so long ago."

"On our way home," she recorded, "we went to Deir Busra, where we are now building a new church and school. I found that the stones were all ready and the bricks are being burnt. We hope to begin school there in the fall. The boys preach there every Sunday now."

December 12, 1933: "The cold days are here and the children are very much in need of more clothes. A little extra money has started coming in and we have been able to begin sewing. But this is only a beginning, for there is still much more needed.

"I am quite well again. I have had over two months of illness and was unable to do a single thing. This illness was a wonderful lesson to me. Many times before I was ill, I would complain when I had to do work which I did not like; but now no matter how much I dislike doing a thing, or how tired I am, I thank God that He has given me the strength to be able fo do it.

"Those two months were very hard for me, as I could see the work piling up and needing to be done, but I was unable to do anything. I promised God that if He would heal me, I would not complain again."

On December 13, 1934, Mama wrote an urgent letter to friends in America: "I wish that I felt stronger to begin the new year. There is so much I would like to do which I fear I am not strong enough to do. My heart is not strong and I now have to be very careful. Pray that the Lord will give me strength to do the work which He would have me do.

". . . About this, the greatest burden of my whole life, won't you pray that the Lord will, in answer to our prayers, send the money needed for the food at least a day in advance. I don't think anyone can imagine the wonderful difference it would mean to me. My body is tired with all the cares of the orphanage, my very large mail to see about, all the visitors to see and the personal care of the little children, with never a real holiday. I did not intend to write this. . . ."

Chapter XI

ONE MID-WINTER morning in 1933 Mama arose at daylight, knelt by her bed, and cried for a long time. When she was completely spent she began to pray softly. Prospects of getting any money seemed hopeless. The year had been hard—unmercifully hard, of late. Famine had swept across the land like the infamous siege of the locusts. Friends in America had been struck hard by the depression and could help very little. The orphanage was deeply in debt—so deeply in debt that the thing Mama had long feared was about to become a reality. For the first time now she faced the fact that she must search for another way of feeding her children and their widowed mothers. Somehow an idea which she must have pushed away many times came to her now in full armor. Before, it had seemed so drastic that she had rejected it. Now she found herself accepting almost docilely. She arose from her knees, hurried to the older girls' dormitory.

"Alya," she said to the girl in charge, "will you please call all the children together in the courtyard after breakfast? Then ask the widows to come a few minutes later." The girl looked surprised. "Yes, Mama," she said. Mama walked slowly back to her rooms then. She must read her Bible and pray. One thing she knew. She could eat no breakfast. An hour later she stood before her children—more than a thousand now. How she dreaded to begin the words she had to say! Somehow she steeled herself, though, took a deep breath and started:

"My children, we are in a hard situation." The young faces in front of her and around her became tense and immobile. Almost at once they sensed the graveness of Mama's tone. "Children," she went on, "there hasn't been sufficient money lately. And there are so many of us to be fed. Therefore, much as I love you, I must—I must send you away. To relatives, if you have any. To friends, if you have no relatives. If you've no friends—" Her voice broke into a sob realizing how many of her brood had no friend except Mama. She fought to keep control of her emotions. "If you've no friends—well, we'll make friends for you."

She hesitated, seeing the astonished, hurt looks on their faces. "My dear children, I will bring you back again when God has supplied our needs." She looked down at the courtyard ground, worn smooth by a thousand playtimes, and more thousands of prayertimes they had shared together in the evenings. She had to look away from her children's eyes. She could not face them. "I promise—" Her voice faded to a sob.

Suddenly she was aware that no one could hear her. Her children were crying, softly at first, then mighty sobs, unreached for, unwanted, but swelling into being anyway. The prospect of having to leave the only home, the only mother, the only security they had ever known, was almost more than they could bear. The shock, delayed at first, seemed to hit them a minute or two after the words were spoken. Mama spoke again, tried to reason with them. But her own voice was choked and broken as she tried to talk, and she could not make herself heard. Suddenly a little boy in the back of the courtyard who had been busily shooting paper wads a moment before, fell to his knees and cried with a loud voice, his small brown hands folded angelically under his chin, "Lord. Lord," he called. As if afraid he wouldn't be heard by the Lord in the midst of the confusion, he called more loudly: "Lord. *Lord! Lord!*" Seemingly satisfied that he had made himself heard by the Lord, he proceeded to vow a vow which must have meant real sacrifice to him. "Lord, I won't ever do anything bad no more. Please, please, please—" Tears rushed down his upturned face. Then another child fell to his knees. Then another. And another. Until everyone in the courtyard was kneeling and praying earnestly.

With great depth it came to Mama that her hundreds of children were doing only what they had seen her do, both in times of plenty and in times of stress. They knew she prayed without ceasing. This, then, she realized, was the only thing the children knew to do in so great an emergency. What greater thing could they do? She looked away from them in pain. Could she stand by in the midst of such faith which she herself had taught them, and see them disappointed? Surely God was hearing their earnest prayers, rendered more earnest by their dire need.

"Lord, my Lord, what now?" she asked earnestly, kneeling quietly with the others. Finally she stood, holding up her arms for attention. The courtyard gradually became quiet again as she gave them their time-honored signal and one pair at a time, all their arms were raised.

"I cannot send you away," she said simply. "I cannot. If we do without, we will do without together. We will all continue to pray that our needs may be met. Perhaps it is good that you, too, know that we live by faith—that God must give us all that we have."

Then she wiped the tears from her face and went to the

big orphanage kitchen. How could she stretch this little remaining rice for a thousand hungry mouths? "Add some more water, Mai," she said to the young widow in charge of the kitchen. "Lots of water. And quarter these slices of bread. We will give each child a quarter of a slice and it will be better than no slice at all. And the cows we have in the back will give us all the milk we can drink, thank the Lord."

"And you, Mama," the widow said. "You must be hungry too. You haven't eaten since yesterday at noon, and then hardly at all."

Mama laughed and said truthfully, "You know, I seem to have lost my appetite."

The prayers in the courtyard that evening were earnest. As usual, Mama read the Bible. When they had finished she went up to her rooms, wrote some letters, had a long talk with two of her girls who were planning to be married, but felt they should not leave Mama until this crisis was past. Then midnight. Wearily, Mama dragged herself to bed, said a hurried prayer, but found herself going to sleep even before she had finished. One thing she knew: From the beginning God had promised to see her through. Hadn't He always kept His word? Hadn't He?

Wearily, she dressed herself the next morning and went down to the kitchen. Three of the cows were fresh. There would be milk for breakfast. The bread was all gone. So were the grocery staples. Later in the morning, when it was time for the mail to come in, she sent one of the boys to the post office in Assiout.

Even the smallest children waited for him to return. Would there, could there be anything from America in the mail? She knew her faithful helpers were not counting on it. No money had come in for days. Only very minute amounts had come in for long weeks.

Had the people back home forgotten them? She shuddered inwardly, outwardly, at an unbidden fear which seemed to take hold of her being. *Had God forgotten?*

Now the boy was coming from the post office. Quickly he ran to Mama and handed her the mail. There was one letter from America. Mama opened it with trembling fingers. She shouted with joy when she looked at it.

It was a check for one thousand dollars!

She studied the address on the envelope: Miss Lillian Trasher, Assiout, India. *India!* She looked at the note with the check, then smiled with relief. This letter was for her, all right. The check, too. A generous Kansas man had simply made a common mistake in addressing the envelope. And the letter with only her name and Assiout, India, written on it, had come straight to her in Assiout, Egypt, without any delay.

Quickly she threw her old blue cape around her shoulders and hurried out the gate toward Assiout. Wheat! Beans! Onions! Rice! Her steps beat out the rhythm that whirled through her being. Wheat. Beans. Onions. Rice. How her hungry children and widows would eat tonight.

Now Mama waved at Said, her farmer neighbor working in his field. Her steps were quick and confident as she crossed the bridge into Assiout. The sun was shining on the Nile waters below. At the bank the American woman's good news spread fast. Mama's faith had proved itself again. She bought the food they needed, then went by the dry goods store and bought a large quantity of cotton cloth. Then, another stop to order a large steer. (It took a large one now to feed her family just one meal if they all had even a small serving of meat); then home, to begin cutting out dresses for her multitude of children. How beautiful her dark-eyed little girls would look in their new dresses! "Bring them in," she called happily. And, ten at a time, the little girls came, in correct order as to size, each about two inches higher than the one before her. In this way, Mama could cut dresses for all the girls that same size in the orphanage. Mama settled down to work in earnest. She would still be cutting the dresses at midnight.

There were long earnest prayers of thanksgiving that night at prayertime in the courtyard. At midnight, Mama laid down her cutting scissors, folded the last dress into the big sewing boxes, wearily undressed, and got into bed. She went to sleep immediately. The orphanage was so large now that the thousand dollars would all be spent in three days, or maybe a week, if she stretched it far enough. If they were running ahead on supplies such an amount might have bought groceries for weeks. But not in their present depleted condition. It took a lot of wheat and rice and beans, even if there was no meat, to feed a thousand people for a day. And for every day, all the time, the amounts had to be enormous to be barely enough. The crisis was past, though. When she had enough food and supplies for three days she felt she had a gracious plenty. Even one day's food and supplies ahead gave her the peace of mind she so desperately needed.

A week later Mama went to the bank to cash a small check that had come in the mail from a nurse in Africa who had once visited the orphanage. It was a check that came in regularly from a small salary. Now Mama needed it badly. The thousand dollars, carefully spent for food and material, was gone now. Most of the food it had bought was gone, too. Now they needed two pounds more if there was to be enough to buy the flour for the next day's bread. Mama stood still in the Assiout bank, awaiting directions. She closed her eyes and continued to wait for instructions. She saw several rich men come in. She asked: "Lord, shall I ask them for help?" It came to her clearly. The answer was "no." They were coming back by her now, and looked at her briefly. Then they hurried on through the door. She stopped smiling. "Lord," she said. "I've *got* to have money for that flour!"

Across the street she visited an elderly lady who had been bedridden for more than a year. Her two daughters were there and they all visited a while, as old friends will. One of the daughters leaned toward Mama. She studied her a minute, then turned, a somber note in her voice. "Mother, our Lillian is not looking well." The old lady looked at Lillian. Then she laughed gently: "I guess I know what is the matter with Lillian. I suspect she has no money for the flour." Then she put her hand under the pillow and drew out two pounds. She handed it to Mama. Then the younger daughter got a similar amount out of her purse. "There," she said. "I, too, feel better now! And Lillian looks better already!"

The following day there was not enough money for flour again. Mama went into a store in Assiout to buy a pair of stockings for one of her girls. She stopped at the piece goods counter to get a yard of cloth to finish the lining of a quilt. As she was leaving, the clerk stopped her. "Something for you, Mama," the man smiled. She looked down to see a pound being put into her palm. With what she had already, there was more than enough to buy the flour for tomorrow's bread.

Another day, she found they were short a half pound for flour, so Mama walked in Assiout, this time to one of the "charity boxes" a friend had installed for her. This charity box was in front of the Nile Club, patronized by well-to-do businessmen and others. Now Mama looked in the box where she often found money to help her. But it was empty. A voice from behind startled her. A friendly voice she recognized from the past. It was a good Egyptian friend who now smiled at her.

"The box seems empty, doesn't it," he said, putting his hand in his pocket and bringing out some silver money. Then, he put the silver change back and brought out a pound note. Then he put that back, laughing, "Lily, I know that isn't enough." She looked down to see her friend handing her four pounds. Four pounds! That would take care of the flour for three or four days with money left over. While they were talking, two young men, friends of both of them, stopped, and each one handed Mama a handful of piasters.

"Perhaps when you read some of my letters," she wrote in a letter to America, "you may get the idea that money just drops on me as I walk along! No, some days are dark and dreary—so hard, so hard. Yet God, in His own time, sees that everything is all right."

In November, 1935, she wrote her friends in America: "I feel so thankful for the little lives which have been given us to care for in His name. On Sunday morning as I sat on the platform of our big lovely church given us by a kind gentleman from Philadelphia, and saw the hundreds of innocent little faces looking to me for bread, love, and for the Bread of Life, and a mother's guiding hand over the hard places, I closed my eyes and bowed my head and prayed: "Lord, help me!"

Again she wrote: "How I need your prayers. These children are just like any other children. Some are ill, some good, some easy to manage, while others give me much trouble and many heartaches. But all must be taught and cared for. The good mothers of America think they have their hands full if they have four or five little ones to care for, with the father to see about the money matters; but I have nearly a thousand and must do both a mother and father's work for all of these. And I must write hundreds of letters each week. Then I must oversee or do all the work. How I love my work and thank God that He chose me and not someone else, but I am so tired. . . ."

Mama wished her friends across America, and the world, could be there and hear the little ones saying their Scripture lessons. Some were so tiny they could not understand. Yet they could say the Lord's Prayer in English and in Arabic and the twenty-third Psalm and many other portions of the Bible. Jesus Himself said, "Suffer the little children to come unto me. . . ."

"Sometimes I get discouraged," she wrote in her diary one night. "But then I remember that if it were not for the open doors of the orphanage, these children would never be able to read as there are no free schools in hundreds of miles. Only a very few are accepted in each school, and our children could not even get this chance, as they would have no one to feed and clothe them or buy their books.

"As I look at my children I feel they are God's gift to me, and, of course, they feel the same: that the Lord sent them a mother from away across the sea. . . . We never turn any child away because we have no money. Or because we have no bed for him. If we feel the child needs the home, we accept him."

Again in her diary: "Someone gave us a lovely gramaphone and some nice records of hymns—'Onward, Christian Soldiers,' 'Joy to the World,' 'Silent Night,' and others. One of the girls puts the records on while we do the cutting and sewing. I am sure that they will never forget these wonderful days together. These are such happy hours—the sacred music, the love all about us, the useful work. . . . Surely my girls will remember these hours long after they have left us and have homes of their own.

"The boys are doing well with the chairmaking. We are getting more orders than we are able to fill. Of course, school takes up most of their time.

"What a sad thing happened: One of our girls, who has been married about ten years and has four little children, came back to us saying her husband has gone blind and that his family would not keep her or the children. Of course we took her in."

In spite of her persistent cheerfulness and her refusal to slow her pace when her great family needed her, Mama began to notice a subtle change in herself that boded no good. The way she had to climb the stairs slowly, or not at all. The way she did without food when she should have been hungry. The way she was tired all the time—even in the mornings when she first awakened. The way sharp pains shot around her heart when she was exhausted. The way her breath left her. The way her throat muscles contracted with tension until she had to lie down to ease them.

Her older girls were doing more of the heavy work now. One of her older boys was helping her immensely by doing much of the clerical work and accounting and shouldering more and more of the administrative load. She loved this boy, Mena Girgis. He was truly a beloved son.

He had come to her a little boy in 1920, shy but lovable and intelligent. For a long time he was just one of the crowd of 1,000. Then one wonderful day Mama suddenly *saw* him. It was love from the first. He would stand by her desk quietly as she worked. He began to help in little ways—then more and more. Later he married one of Mama's little girls —Mary. [He became business manager of the orphanage when a very young man.]

Her older girls were doing more of the heavy work now. The widows were most helpful as far as they knew how to be. But often there was no one there when a hard job had to be done. Often no one but Mama could take the tremendous responsibilities that were involved in just one decision.

By now there were more than eleven hundred in the orphanage and of necessity most of the heaviest responsibilities had to fall on Mama's tired shoulders and heart. She knew her friends in Assiout were worrying and knew they were trying to help her even more than they had in the past. But times were so hard that it was difficult for anyone to give much. She loved these dear Egyptian friends. Often she thought: "I had to come all the way to Egypt to get to call you my friends!"

Still she grew more tired. Sometimes she could hardly get up the stairs.

Today was especially cold and bleak, late in February of 1937. Her somber spirits matched the day. She was so tired—so tired—that she felt if she sat down she would surely stay forever. Then a sharp young voice. It was a telegraph delivery boy at the door. "Mama! Mama!" His tones were excited, happy, as he called, then began reeling off a string of Arabic in his joy. He thrust an envelope toward her. It was a cablegram sent from a steamer off the west coast of Africa. When she read it, Mama sank into a nearby rocker and closed her eyes. Tears of weariness and tears of gratitude mingled freely on her cheeks. The cablegram was from Lord Maclay, a Scots nobleman. But more than his prominent position and title, he was a kind, dear friend of Mama's who had come into her life just when she needed a friend the most. Her eyes closed, her lips smiling, Mama's mind flashed back through the years.

An Egyptian woman, a friend of Mama's, had invited her home with her for dinner, and though Mama rarely accepted an invitation to leave her children she welcomed this chance to be with her friend for an hour. As usual, her cares at the orphanage were increased by the lack of money to buy food the next day. Somehow getting the daily flour and other necessary food seemed too difficult for her lately.

They had barely finished when they heard the whistle of the Nile luxury steamer that plied its way from Cairo with its load of pleasure-seeking tourists. Mama quickly excused herself. She must get to the orphanage for her pamphlets, then hurry to the steamer which she knew would stop over in Assiout for refueling and to allow the passengers time to shop for the black nose veils they could take back as souvenirs. Of course, most Egyptian women had stopped wearing the veils. They were uncomfortable and scratchy even for tourists to wear for a short time. But they must have something to take home to show that they had been somewhere. So the ship, which needed time for refueling anyway, stopped at Assiout.

Mama quickly said goodbye to her hostess, who was shaking her head at her American friend now. "Your orphans always come first, don't they?" Mama made long strides down the street toward the barrage which formed the bridge to the orphanage. She could see the steamer anchoring at the shore. And she hurriedly got the pamphlets telling of the huge orphanage run by "faith," moved quickly up the gangplank. Breathless from her fast walk, she stopped a moment on the deck trying to decide which group of laughing, talking sightseers to approach first. "Lord, I'm listening," she said. But she felt no answer. Perhaps she was hurrying too much. She moved toward the tables where the passengers were having tea, then stopped at one table. "Would any of you be interested in reading about the Assiout Christian orphanage run by faith where there are nearly a thousand children?" She studied their faces. How empty the young women's eyes appeared. How hard the young men's set, white faces. Thinking they hadn't heard her she began again: "Would any of you care—?" Now the young man nearest her turned abruptly, blew cigarette smoke straight into her face with sharp deliberation. Through the smoke she could see him: harsh lines around the mouth, deep black circles under his eyes, a sneering glance. "No! I would not care—" He glared insolently at her, then turned away. But he had told the truth, Mama realized. He truly did "not care."

She moved away, a little chagrined by such treatment. Usually she was accepted when she did her "asking" for her children. Even when the Egyptian people had nothing to give her financially, they gave her kind, mannerly treatment. She was hardly a few steps from the young fellow who had rebuffed her when she heard a soft, mellow voice. The warm sound of it seemed to melt the icy treatment she had just received. "Just a moment—" The voice came closer. "I would very much like to see one of your booklets." Mama turned to see a beautiful face framed with soft, reddish-blond hair. The lips were smiling kindly. But most of all Mama saw the eyes. They were gentle. She handed the young woman the pamphlets, grateful that she had come to her when she did. Now her new friend was showing a group the stories and pictures of the orphanage. Mama went quietly to the other side of the deck and waited. Shortly, she saw the young woman coming to her. She handed Mama five dollars. "I am Lady Inskip of Scotland," she said, smiling again. "May I come this evening to see your orphanage?"

Mama smiled broadly, surprised. She hurried home to get everything ready for her lovely, titled guest.

By seven o'clock the kitchen was shining, the entire place was immaculate. The younger children had been bathed and put to bed.

Promptly at eight a knock sounded at the door, and Mama opened it and welcomed the lovely young woman she had met. With her was a tall sandy-haired Scotchman who appeared to be around twenty-five or thirty years older than Lady Inskip. Mama took his hat. "Miss Trasher—my father, Lord Maclay," she said. Mama hardly knew what to do. Or what to say, either. Never had she been around nobility before, and she told her guests so.

The young woman laughed. So did her father. Then he looked directly into Mama's eyes. "Miss Trasher, whatever titles I might have shrink to nothing compared with your character and nobility."

Mama showed them through the orphanage then. She was proud of her children. She was happy that everything was in its place, neat and clean.

When Lord Maclay was leaving, he handed Mama twenty pounds. After that the generous Scotch nobleman and his family sent them money every Christmas—sometimes as much as fifty pounds.

Now Mama rose from her rocking chair, read the cablegram she had received from him once more. Lord Maclay was coming through Cairo on business, but his schedule was so heavy that he wouldn't have time to come to Assiout. Could Mama meet him at Cairo the following morning and while his ship refueled and loaded, they could talk.

Could she!

Busily Mama readied herself for the trip. She decided to drive and Jennie, who was with her at the orphanage again, agreed to go with her.

When she met the Scots nobleman on the dock in Cairo, she showed him her photographs of her children. There was one of the new babies, another of the "middle" babies, one of the toddlers, another of the newest addition, and one of the older boys doing leathercraft. And here the younger girls were sewing beside Mama in her rocking chair under the big tree in the front.

He thought they were lovely pictures and said so. "But what I wanted to know," he said, "is there anything you are especially in need of?"

Well, the children were badly in need of clothes. And flour—it was such a burden from day to day to find the money to buy the flour for their bread. She felt, too, that her children needed more meat than they were getting.

"And how about you?" Her friend was looking curiously at her now, smiling an incredulous smile she didn't understand. "How about you?" he asked again." Don't you *ever* need *anything* for yourself?"

The question was so unexpected that it caught Mama completely off guard. She smiled a little, realizing that she had thought of her multitudes of children and widows so long that she actually couldn't think of a single thing she needed for herself. Now she said: "No, I am all right. But my children—" A flood of wishes poured in upon her when she thought of her children and their great needs. Her voice broke. She stopped, then, and wiped her eyes with a clean white handkerchief Jennie had handed her when she had left the car moments before.

"Miss Trasher, I am going to give you a thousand pounds —five thousand dollars in American money."

Mama closed her eyes as her Scots friend spoke. She suddenly heard bells ringing. Through the bells she heard his voice as a distant, melodious sound. Five thousand dollars! She was afraid to open her eyes for a moment for fear she had been dreaming. But he was continuing very realistically by writing a check. As he wrote it, she thought: Oh the cows, the clothes, the rice, the onions, the beans, the beef, the flour that five thousand dollars would buy! Her children would thrive. She tried to open her eyes, to thank her bene-factor, but found that she could not control her tears when she did so.

"But—" His voice was almost stern now. And surprised, she looked at him sitting there so straight and stern in his deck chair, the bright sunlight catching red and gold glints in his graying hair. "I want you to use a portion of this for yourself—half of it. I ask you, please. For just once use this amount for yourself."

But what did she need for herself? She smiled a little, try-ing hard to think of anything she wanted for herself. She could think of nothing. Well, nothing except— Ridicu-lously, her mind went back to the restaurant window in Long Beach, California, to a luscious-looking lemon me-ringue pie.

"Thank you, my good friend," she said. The steamer whis-tle blew. They stood and shook hands. Then he was hurry-ing up the gangplank and she was walking toward the car where Jennie was waiting. Happily she showed Jennie the check. "Let's go by town in Assiout and buy a steer so that all the children can have meat tonight. Then we need quilt material. We can stop by—"

"Lill," Jennie interrupted softly. "Lill, do you suppose we could spend a few pennies of the five thousand dollars for—for—"

"For what, Jen? Go on." She saw her soft-voiced sister hesitate, then look steadily into her eyes.

"Do you think we could buy a box of chocolates for me to parcel out to the little ones?"

Mama gave her sister a quick hug. "How you do spoil them," she said. "And how I love you for it!"

Mama awakened early the next morning feeling a good sense of well-being and satisfaction. Even exuberance. After breakfast she answered a knock at the door. It was the same messenger boy who had brought her the cablegram two mornings before. He seemed even more excited this time, if this were possible. He handed her an envelope once again, then left in staccato, off-beat rhythm. Trembling, she opened it, read it, then retraced the words therein once more with her eyes. Surely she must have read it wrongly the first time. But, no. She sank to the floor in prayer. Finally she leaned her body against the old rocker which always stayed by the front door, rested her head on its arm and cried for a long time.

She had no idea how long she stayed there that way. She heard some of her girls come in, felt them help her up the stairs to her rooms and gently put her in her bed. Some time later, she didn't know how long, she awakened dully. The doctor from the American hospital was checking her pulse and she opened her eyes and smiled at him. What had she ever done to deserve such kind treatment? She tried to open her mouth to speak, to thank him, to help him understand that she was really all right. But he gently shook his head at her, put his finger to his lips and patted her on the shoulder. She was to rest a few days and he was sure she would be all right. Then he left. The girls slipped out, too.

She stared at her right hand, still clenched tightly. In it was the cablegram. Carefully she opened her hand, smoothed the cablegram and read it again silently. Then she breathed a deep sigh and closed her eyes happily trying to absorb the magnitude of the words therein.

Lord Maclay had decided to send *another* four thousand

pounds. The money was on its way. That made five thousand pounds—in those days twenty-five thousand dollars.

It meant rest for her weary body and her aching heart. The news had been almost more than she had been able to take. She closed her eyes.

Now the sun slid from sight, the night struck swiftly, as it always did here in the desert country. The beautiful Egyptian moon rose, majestic, bright, but gentle.

Mama turned her sleeping face full to Egypt's ancient, mysterious moonlight on the Nile and began to dream. The future seemed bright and far easier. Then she frowned abruptly. In the distance a dark cloud appeared on the desert horizon. This was indeed strange. Egyptian skies were cloudless skies except when the khamsin winds came in the spring bringing desert dust in them. This cloud was coming closer. It was a vile thing in her dream. Now it crept slowly across the sky like a mighty monster with a lashing tail. She cried out, then impatiently brushed the dream away with a sharp gesture. Everything was sure to go well at the orphanage now since Lord Maclay's magnificent gift. The years ahead were going to be bright and wonderful. How could they be otherwise?

Chapter XII

THE AUTUMN of 1947, time of terror and death, was upon Egypt.

Mama had faced springtime cheerfully, as usual, not knowing what was to come. World War II had brought a shipload of Red Cross supplies originally intended for Greece. But that country had fallen into enemy hands and the American ambassador had given the shipload of clothing to Mama, together with a hundred-and-twenty-five-dollar check to pay the shipping costs from Cairo. She had been grateful, for her children were in need. How could she possibly express her thanks? Two thousand six hundred dresses, nineteen hundred woolen sweaters of all sizes, blankets, foodstuffs, and many more pieces of clothing! In addition, the American government had begun sending surplus foods to help Mama and her great Egyptian family which by now had multiplied until it numbered over twelve hundred. Also, the Women's Missionary Council of the Assemblies of God had sent an unusual amount of clothing for both widows and children. Individual Christians of that Church had sent their gifts faithfully, too.

Still, Mama had to manage to make the food go around and by the middle of the summer she began to conserve supplies even more carefully. By late summer she found her money and food supplies running dangerously low again. She was busily trying to make ends meet when one day something appeared which was to occupy her mind much more predominately. That something came in September. It was a terror which came without warning. This terror which now stalked Egypt was far more terrible than food and clothing shortages. It was a terror so great that even Mama lived in constant dread of it. It moved across Egypt like a monster with a thousand deadly fangs and a tail of death. Whenever the monster stopped at a house, a circle of white paint was spread on the front door by soldiers who then took up their guard at a distance. The white circle of death struck terror in the hearts of passers-by and caused them to hurry in the other direction in fear of their lives. For the white painted door meant that there was horrible, stinking, living death inside. Living death, then still, silent death. *Cholera death!*

Generally, the family of the victim had the death within them in a few hours. And in a short time there was only the white paint smear on the front door as a reminder that a family had once lived there.

The terrible cholera siege of Egypt began in September of 1947 and soon hundreds were dying of it—by November, thousands. At first, it avoided Assiout where Mama lived with her big family. But then it began to creep closer. Mama looked at her masses of children packed into the orphanage so closely that any contagious disease would spread like wildfire. She shuddered with apprehension when she thought about it. Always she would pray, not only that the cholera would not get past the gates, but that her fear would be taken away. How she longed for Jennie in times of fear like this, but Jennie was back in America. It had been nearly nine years now since her beloved older sister had visited

Egypt. It was a lonely time of secret longing for Mama. If she hadn't been so terribly busy she would have been more lonesome and more frightened. Too, Jennie had promised to come back this Christmas. That wasn't too long distant. Already November had arrived. She smiled to herself in spite of her fears.

On November 14, 1947, Mama wrote friends in the Assemblies of God churches in America: ". . . There has been very little money coming in, but such things are not as important as other greater things. You have most likely heard of the cholera which struck Egypt September 23, 1947. Thousands have died with it . . . it spreads so fast and kills within a few hours. . . . We opened our school early in October but I expect that we are about the only school open in Egypt. The government has been obliged to close all schools because of the awful epidemic of cholera . . . hundreds die every day. We did not close our school, as, of course, our children are orphans and have no place to go. . . . The doctors are all very busy trying to inject school children."

The day after Mama and Alya were sorting dress scraps into the quilting boxes in Mama's workroom. Mama looked up thoughtfully and said, "Perhaps I shouldn't accept any new ones in the orphanage until the cholera danger is past." She frowned a little, worriedly. "But never have I turned any one away in need. It would break my heart to have to say 'No' to a hungry, sick child."

Alya did not answer. There didn't seem to be any answer. It was a bright, sunny morning at the orphanage. The light, coming through the broad east windows, cast iridescent rays on Alya's long, black hair. The dark eyes shone with the warmth and beauty of Egypt's alluringly beautiful women of all the ages. How this lovely Egyptian girl reminded Mama of Fareida who had been her firstborn! Those dark eyes were very much like Fareida's. Fareida! She thought again of how they had gone together to the big rented house to begin their lives anew. Mama smiled in remembrance. She had been very bold to step out on that mighty adventure with the tiny, starving infant. Her very first baby. She thought again of her great joy when Fareida first needed more milk than she could get in the eye dropper. It had been thrilling to see her develop into a plump, healthy baby, then into a beautiful little girl with gay, dark eyes that twinkled at her benefactor. Mama brushed the tears from her eyes now, remembering Fareida. She studied Alya a moment. It seemed she could see the dark eyes of Fareida in this lovely girl who had come after her firstborn. Alya had become like a daughter to Mama, and they were very close. The quilting scraps, for instance. Mama had come in from breakfast to find Alya sorting them—because she saw the need for it. Often she would bring Mama her old blue cape at the nightly prayertime in the courtyard, even before Mama realized she was getting too cool.

Now Mama rose, went to her desk, and began writing a newsletter home to her church friends in America. She wanted to tell her friends about Alya, to remember Fareida. Instead she must tell them about her financial problems. For once, Mama hesitated, put down her pen.

"Alya," she said gently, "how would I get along without you, my dear?"

Alya smiled, went on working. Finally she looked up. There was a trace of tears about her eyes. "Mama, I have loved every minute of my life with you. I want you to know that I love you as my Mama."

Mama felt her eyes brimming over. She wiped them with a quick, impatient stroke, but not quickly enough for the sensitive Alya.

"Mama, did I make you cry?" The beautiful dark eyes, fringed with their long, curling, black lashes, were half smiling, half serious. Mama shook her head.

"I'm glad you told me, dear. I knew, of course. But I am so glad you said it. It makes up for the difficult days that have to come because—well, because of so many things." Mama sighed. "Today, even—" She went back to writing America for her money needs.

"Dear kind friends," she wrote. "Thank you for your help. Never before have I felt His presence so real. . . . " When she had finished, she signed the newsletter: "I am your sister, Lillian Trasher." Then she hurried to Assiout to buy some supplies.

On her way back, she noticed a soldier standing near the door of a small hut near the barrage road. Looking past, she saw the cause of the guard. An ugly white circle of paint had been smeared on the door! Mama hugged the heavy bundles to her, staring. All her fears bore down on her in a mighty, pregnant instant. The circle of white paint meant only one thing! She began to hurry faster to the orphanage. Faster! Faster! Faster! Cholera had come to Assiout! She ran inside, closed the main door and locked it. *"Neither shall any plague come nigh thy dwelling."*

She then went to her rooms and finally gathered her thoughts and knelt beside her bed to pray. Money she needed to run the orphanage seemed relatively unimportant beside this grim sign she had just beheld. Still, life must go on. She knelt again at daybreak the next morning.

"Neither shall any plague come nigh thy dwelling." When she arose her mind was calmed and she began to dress for church, wondering how she would manage the food for tomorrow. Always, the food problem seemed to come to the top when her needs were scrambled, because it was so pressing and always so terribly immediate.

After the Sunday service an Egyptian man walked into the church, smiling broadly. "I was out for a ride," he said, "and wondered how you were getting along." Mama saw him reach in his pocket and hand her several pounds. She closed her eyes in a quick prayer of thankfulness. The food! The food would be on the tables tomorrow!

The following Monday, she went downstairs to do her morning's work. The letter she had written Saturday was ready to be mimeographed with a few additions she had made before breakfast, but it would be midnight before she had time to do it.

The day passed busily, uneventfully. Then evening. And early night. Then, midnight.

She had finished the mimeographing, undressed, knelt for her prayers, then relaxed on her bed drowsily when she became aware of a strange light outside. It was a weird, irregular light, disappearing and coming back. Gradually it grew brighter. At first she thought she must be dreaming. Surely she had gone to sleep and the strange, bright glare was only a nightmare. She roused herself when she heard shouts, then the school bell clanging furiously. In the bright jagged glare she hurried to the east windows and cried out at what she saw.

Great mountains of flames shot into the sky from the boys' dormitory. It seemed every window was filled with the eerie glare of the flames hurtling out into the night. With a sharp cry, Mama slipped into her shoes and robe, called the fire department, and ran down the stairs and across the yard. She knew forty small boys were sleeping in the upstairs wing where the fire seemed to be the worst. Where were they? She ran toward one of her big boys.

"Mena," she screamed into the noise and flames, "we must go in and get them!" With fear gripping every fiber within her, she began to run toward the flames, searching for the most logical place to slip inside. Her eyes lighted on a door with no fire in it. She was almost to it when she felt a strong arm seize her about the waist.

"Mama," a hoarse voice gasped. "They're all out. Believe me, we got every one of them out." She turned to see Mena, his handsome face covered with soot and his clothes soaking wet with perspiration.

"Are you sure? Are you absolutely sure, Mena?" Mama cried.

"Yes, Mama, yes. There were forty boys in there. And we got forty out. They are safe in the courtyard. See?" And Mena hurried off. Mama looked across the yard to see her little boys, their eyes wide with excitement, waving to her. With desperate calmness, despite her hurry, she began walking toward them, walking and counting heads.

The big boys had thrown all the burning mattresses outside. Mama's methodical and desperate eyes searched the Assiout road for the fire engine once more. There was no sign of it yet. What could be taking it so long? She sighed

wearily. The man who took the call must have gone back
to sleep without turning in the alarm.

She hurried to the big boys who were beating on the flaming mattresses with sticks and brooms. "Break into the storeroom and get those new buckets," she cried over the noise
of the crackling fire and the shouts of the hard-working boys.
"There are a hundred and fifty new buckets in there. Quick!
Get them! Form a brigade!"

A group of the big boys, hearing her commanding voice,
quickly heeded her. In moments a water bucket brigade
was operating with such precision and efficiency that it was
almost like a steady stream of water pouring into the burning areas of the building. Mama sighed. It seemed as if all
would be under control in a matter of minutes. Then, a
stray bit of flame flashed onto the far side of the kitchen. In
an instant there was a mass of flame there spreading wildly.

"To the kitchen," Mama screamed. "Go to the kitchen
with the buckets!" The line of buckets turned to the kitchen.
Again Mama relaxed for an instant. She wiped off the
perspiration streaming down her face and realized that her
face, too, was covered with soot, as were her clothes. She
looked down at herself in the glare. The dirt and smoke
completely covered her. She closed her eyes and cried an
unheard sob. She longed for the quiet comfort of Jennie
at such a grim moment. But Jennie would be back. She had
written she was coming to Egypt again from her home in
Long Beach, California, and would arrive at Christmastime.
Mama ran a hand over her grimy face. Anyway, she thought,
there would be plenty of hot water when this was over, and
they would begin immediately cleaning up. Fortunately the
kerosene tanks which provided the heat for their hot water

were well filled—*the kerosene tanks!* Now Mama's thoughts burned within her. The kerosene tanks were at the far edge of the kitchen. If the flames reached there, there would be terrible explosions, the fire would spread to other buildings, and worse, some of her boys fighting the fire might be killed or badly hurt. Her eyes searched the far wall for a trace of the flames spreading there. Once more, she desperately searched the Assiout road for the fire engine. But there was still no sign of it. "Hurry, hurry," she called to the panting, exhausted boys. How weak and helpless she felt. Suddenly she realized that her boys were moving as quickly and efficiently as humanly possible. They were working like mad to save their home. Water was pouring methodically over every burning area with the greatest concentration being on the kitchen area nearest the kerosene tanks.

"What shall I do? What shall I do?" It was a cry born of utter desperation. And it was lost in the confusion. She fell to her knees, astonished that she had been so busy looking after the spreading flames that she had forgotten to pray. She was so weak with the strain, however, that she could not seem to pray adequately. She closed her eyes. The words finally came:

"Do something, Lord," she begged. "Do something—the kerosene tanks— Do something, Lord!"

Moments later she became aware that the fire was lessening in degree. Finally she could see no flames, not even any sparks. But the weary boys continued to watch for any new outbreaks. When the fire engine arrived a few minutes later, the fire was completely out. Shortly after daybreak the ambulance arrived from Assiout, offering to take the injured to the hospital. Black, sooty tears streamed down Mama's face. She looked steadily at the ambulance drivers.

"No one—not *one* was hurt," she said, her voice choked with emotion.

When it was light enough for her to see she examined the wall next to the kerosene storage tanks. A window in the wall was open and old newspapers had been stuffed in it at some time. She stared at the window: the flames had eaten right up to the dry newspapers, *then stopped!* Just beyond the window were the tanks filled with the deadly explosive kerosene.

"Thank you, Lord," she whispered. Then she went to her rooms for a bath and clean clothes. Immediately after, she sat down at her desk to write another newsletter home to her Assemblies of God friends. It would take help—lots of help—to rebuild. Also, she had to figure out how they would eat until the kitchen could be rebuilt. An hour later, she went to the big kitchen, still trembling and smoking from its ordeal. All was quiet here now. Nearly everyone had gone back to sleep now that the danger seemed to be over. She looked at the stove. Perhaps it was still usable. Two of the worktables seemed all right, or would be with a little work on the burned legs.

Mama sat down on a scorched workbench and put her palms over her eyes as if trying to shut out the sight of the ruins. Somehow, she must determine what was usable in the charred pile of rubble, then, some way, she must find the means to replace what was lost and rebuild the building. It wouldn't have seemed so hard when she was young. But now— She rose, tried to walk across the debris-filled kitchen, stumbled, and almost fell over a pile of rubble. For the first time she realized that she was too exhausted to think clearly. She looked up through the great, gaping holes in the roof and tears filled her eyes. "I'll certainly need Your help Lord," she cried quietly.

A few mornings later, Mama awakened to the sound of knocking on the main gate. It was a dreary sound, persistent, fading, then returning like a bad dream. She heard Alya going to answer, then the girl's steps sounded more loudly as she came back toward Mama's rooms. "It's a poor man and his two little boys," Alya told her. "They are ragged and so hungry and tired. I told them we could not take anyone at present due to the cholera epidemic, but they have walked for four days through the desert and—"

Mama sighed wearily. Never had she turned away anyone in need, but now with deadly cholera striking in every quarter and with such contagion, she felt it was unfair to the children to take anyone new. A new child might have been contaminated. So she had made the rule a few days before to be in effect for the duration of the cholera epidemic in Egypt. *No one admitted!*

Those were cold, cruel words—institutional, antiseptic words. But what else could she do in the wake of such a monstrous killer as cholera? Now she raised her head, looked steadily at Alya almost in anger that such a decision should be forced on her. Her voice was harsh. "Tell them 'No.' Positively 'No'!" The girl looked startled at her tone, then turned and walked down the hall. Mama heard her steps on the stairs. No. Positively no! No place for you because you might be sick. You need us. You need God. You need love, food, kindness, but "no," positively "no." You can't come in. Like a record with the needle stuck in the groove, her words echoed back hollowly: "You can't come in. You can't come in. No place for you because you might be sick. You need us. You need God. You need love, food, kindness, but 'no,' you can't come in."

Suddenly she was running down the hall, down the stairs, to the door, to the gate. "Alya! Wait, Alya!" At the main gate she jerked herself to a halt and stared. Before her a weary man stood dejectedly in ragged, dirty clothing. Beside him two little boys looked up at her in misery. They couldn't have been more than five or six years old, yet in their eyes lay the sorrow of the ages. Their mother had died —there was no food—hope was gone.

"Let them in," Mama said hoarsely. She sighed tiredly. "We will hope I have acted wisely."

Alya led the two weary children inside for baths and food. Mama sent the father to the kitchen so he could eat before beginning his long journey home. The little boys were fed, bathed, and put to bed to get some much needed rest. Both of them were exhausted and went to sleep at once. But shortly after midnight Mama heard a great commotion in the smaller boys' dormitory. In a daze she saw Alya running toward her looking tense and worried. Little Musa, the younger boy, was violently ill. Diarrhea, vomiting, high fever. Mama stared at Alya, still half asleep. *The symptoms of cholera!* "Oh my God, my God, what have I done?" cried Mama. "What shall I do now?" she whispered hoarsely. She dressed hurriedly, telling Alya to call the doctor at once. On her way to the boys' building she said a quick prayer. When she arrived she found little Musa had vomited on the bedding and on two of the girls who were caring for him, spreading the dreaded germs—if this were cholera—to them, and through them to untold hundreds of other children.

"If I did wrong, I'm sorry, Lord," Mama prayed desperately. "Help me now. Help me. I simply couldn't turn them away."

A short time later the doctor from the American hospital had diagnosed little Musa's illness. His voice was grave, his eyes registered extreme concern. Cholera! Even though she expected this diagnosis, Mama winced when it came.

The little boy died the same day and the health department came and fumigated the entire building. Every inch was sprayed with strong disinfectant. Every child was vaccinated. Guards were posted at the gates so that no one could enter or leave. Near midnight Mama dragged herself to bed, so weary that she hardly knew what she was doing. "Lord, please. If You please. Don't let even one of my dear ones get cholera." It was too late to save little Musa, but now the lives of a thousand others were at stake. Mama dropped off to a restless sleep.

She prayed almost constantly the next day. How she worked! On her hands and knees she scrubbed the floors and woodwork with a strong disinfectant. Side by side, she and the widows and the older girls scrubbed. As she scrubbed she prayed: "Lord, help." Push, pull back. "Lord, help." Push, pull back. "Lord, help." Push, pull back. Hour after weary hour.

When she arose early the next morning, she failed to hear Alya and when they gathered for breakfast the girl wasn't there. As soon as Mama had assigned chores for the morning and checked the food supply, she went to the little room where Alya slept. The shades were drawn making it very dark, but when her eyes had become accustomed to the darkness she saw the girl's form under the sheet and the dark hair streaming across the pillow. She went quickly to her, laid her hand on her brow. "Alya," she said gently. "Alya!" she called more urgently. *Alya!*" The girl's face was so hot Mama's hand felt almost as if she had burned it by touching her. "Alya!" Now Mama's feet were running down the hall to the telephone. When the doctor was called she ran to the kitchen for cool water and clean rags to cool the fever. What else could she do? She straightened the sheet, the pillow, pressed the wan hand that lay limp and outstretched on the bed. Deliriously Mama's mind flashed back to that first night she had seen Fareida's young mother: her hand—it had been outstretched like this in apparent abandon of life itself a few minutes before she had died. Just as Alya's hand—

"Alya. Oh, Alya. What have I done to you?" She wept soundlessly. Wasn't there anything she could do for this one who was dearer to her than life itself? Wasn't there some little thing? Why, yes. Mama's mind eased. In her panic she had forgotten the only thing she *could* do. She had forgotten to pray. Quickly she fell to her knees by the bed, holding the girl's burning hand in hers. But when she tried to speak, the muscles of her throat contracted until she felt she would choke. A great feeling of weakness spread through her, possessed her completely. She fell to the floor, unconscious.

The sun was streaming into her bedroom window when she awoke. How many hours or days had she slept? At least three days, she felt. Hadn't there been three daylight times?

And three nighttimes? She relaxed for a peaceful, quiet moment. Then, like a brutal, paralyzing shot, memory sent a searing bullet back into her consciousness. Alya! Mama gathered her strength and in a mighty effort called: "Alya! *Alya!*" But there was no response.

She called again, forcing her voice even more. Then, a sound. Or did she imagine it? Yes, it was a sound. She was aware then that the doorknob was turning slowly. Very slowly. She saw a hand, slender and graceful, holding the knob and her eyes followed an upward line to see a pale, thin figure with beautiful, sad eyes. But there were deep circles under them. The figure before her barely moved, sliding one foot in front of the other unsteadily as she walked. Mama gasped. Was she seeing a ghost? Could this be—?

"Alya! Alya!" It was a joyous cry. The slender arms wrapped themselves around Mama gently. The lips, thin and drawn, kissed her. Mama began to cry softly. "Alya, I was afraid. I thought you were a ghost. Is it—is it really you?"

The girl nodded and smiled for the first time. But Mama's mind persisted on an ugly thought: "The cholera—did it—? Was it cholera? Of course it wasn't cholera, or you wouldn't be here, alive."

The girl didn't answer.

Suddenly Mama felt herself growing fearful, uncertain, full of frightening doubts. Was she conscious? Was this only a dream? This wasn't Alya. This was a ghost. She sat up in the bed and screamed hysterically. Alya was dead! *Dead! And she had killed her!*

Great sobs racked Mama's body. Why, oh why had she let the two little boys come into the orphanage? Why hadn't she followed the rule against taking new children during the cholera epidemic? She herself had made the rule and she had been the first to break it. Now, because she had allowed the new ones to come in, she had lost the one who was dearest of all to her. How could she possibly go on now? What was there left? When her sobs had subsided, she wiped her wet face with a towel she found folded on a table by her bed. Then she reached for a glass of water on the far side of the table, feeling very thirsty and tired. In her awkward effort to reach the glass she knocked it slightly, and suddenly, to her great joy, she saw the same slender hand reach out swiftly and steady the glass. Then the hand gave it to her, helping her hold the glass to her lips so she could drink the contents.

Mama's eyes looked up as she drank. And suddenly all the fear left her. Alya smiled at her, and spoke for the first time:

"Do not be afraid, Mama. It is I."

Smiling, Mama closed her eyes to rest. She felt tired, terribly tired. Finally she dozed. Evening came quietly. The chilling night air was refreshing.

"Do not be afraid, Mama. It is I." Now she saw a great radiance. With awe she realized that the figure before her was her Lord. She looked more closely. The lips were smiling comfortingly. Mama felt an aura of peace and goodness in the room. She sighed contentedly. Everything would be all right now that her Lord was near. She caught a quick glimpse into the future.

The kitchen, which the big boys were working to rebuild, was all finished. The pantry was completely stocked with food staples. In the air was the aroma of lamb stew. In the stew pot was enough for nearly thirteen hundred people. Upstairs in the little boys' dormitory all the burned mattresses had been replaced by clean new ones.

And to make everything perfect was the knowledge that her beloved Jennie was on the way. The quiet, loving comfort her older sister would bring was something wonderful to contemplate. This time, Jennie was coming to stay. And the time was almost here. Mama sighed with anticipation and smiled to herself. All was well. As always, she prayed, and listened.

After a while she sighed dreamily, then turned her sleeping face full to Egypt's mysterious moonlight on the Nile and smiled at what she saw in a secret dream. In an instant she was far from Egypt and ten years old again back in the little deep-south coastal town of Brunswick, Georgia, in America. Now she was riding good old Daisy bareback across the fields to Jerdy's house. The old horse slowed to an easy trot and Jerdy, her bosom pal, made a fast leap and slid on behind her. "Let's go swimmin'," they yelled as one, the way they thought. A quick cloud of dust and the two girls were off for the river. An hour passed fast and they boarded old Daisy again, refreshed and eager for further action. "Let's hunt nuts," Lily yelled. "Yeee-eee—ho!" Jerdy responded shrilly, and bouncing jubilantly up and down with Daisy's lumbering gait, they headed for a secret grove of trees at the edge of town.

That was the year Lily would never forget.

Postscript

A NEAT WHITE cottage with climbing vines and flowers around the door adjoins the Assiout Orphanage today. There in the midst of the shading fruit trees lives Mama. The cottage, the fruit trees and the two and a half additional acres—all were given Mama by Jennie, her sister who didn't feel led to be a missionary, but traveled around the world with her love. In 1957, Jennie bought a villa for Mama and herself in beautiful Alexandria. And each summer now when it is the hottest (often 120 degrees in the shade of the regal date palms) the two go there together for six weeks, taking a few of the children with them who have never gotten to see the ocean, and relaxing in the cool breezes which the big Mediterranean sends across the tiered, circular "harbor of safe return" built by Alexander the Great long before Christ was born. Jennie, who went back and forth to visit Lillian through the years, now lives in Egypt with her sister.

There are now thirteen brick, stucco-covered buildings, the last two of which were built by funds raised by the Assemblies of God people with a film on Mama's work. There is a boys' dormitory which covers half an acre (the first unit of which was built in 1916), a large swimming pool given by the Maurice Bey Doss family of Egypt, the stables which house the milk cows, a beautiful church given by a generous Philadelphian, and a nursery. This cottage is very close to Mama's. The two cottages are twins, you could say. Always, Mama had dreamed of having her babies in a cottage near her so she could watch after them more personally and so that they could play on the good earth and in the sunshine. There is a telephone in Mama's cottage, in addition to the one in the main dormitory, so that she can sleep all night without interruption—unless, of course, the girls in charge of the babies call her for help, or an emergency occurs to one or another of the 1275 children and widows who now call this their home, or unless a weary, homeless waif knocks on the door asking for admittance in the night.

The daily struggle for flour is gone. Through the years Mama's friends have helped her individually all they could, often at great personal sacrifice. And the Women's Missionary Council of the Church has sent barrels of clothing, bedding, sewing materials, and financial gifts as often as possible. Parcels now come from CARE and money comes from Mama's friends throughout Egypt and the world. Annually, in the province where Mama's orphanage is located the governor proclaims a day for public subscriptions to help finance the orphanage. Whatever help comes to her, though—or doesn't come—Mama keeps on. One tremendous help which began a trend toward easier times for Mama was the huge Red Cross shipment bound for Greece in World War II which was turned to Mama by the American Ambassador with a personal check to cover shipping charges from Cairo to Assiout.

When word was received that the German army was entering Alexandria during World War II, Mama's American and English friends had to leave because of the impending danger. Mama felt she simply could not leave, however, because of her great family. So she stayed, and prayed that the war would come no closer. The German army never got beyond Alexandria, and Mama didn't interrupt a single task at the orphanage.

When she returned to Egypt from America in September, 1955, she was overwhelmed by the reception the children gave her. For months she had toured the United States speaking in churches in behalf of her orphanage. So she was weary, though very happy when she arrived in Assiout.

"I tried to walk, but could hardly move," she recorded. A thousand children all were trying to hug her at the same time. "Mama, Mama," they chanted in their joy until it became a lovely song. "Mama *jet*, Mama *jet*," they laughed as they came running. "Mama *jet*, Mama has come!"

Finally she got to her room and closed the door. From her big upstairs window she could look down on her huge family filled with happiness at her return.

"I really got lost as I went through all the new rooms which Brother Crouch and Mena have made since I left," she wrote. "And the Crouchs' new baby is just too lovely for words! Most of my thirty-five babies whom I told you could not walk are not only walking, but are running all over the place! And new babies have filled their empty beds! You know I always told you 'Americans' that the trouble with you folks is, 'You just don't have enough children to really make it wonderful!' . . . I wonder if it will not be something like this in Heaven. Sometimes God doesn't make us wait to die before we enter Heaven.' "

As the 1950's passed, the flow of her letters to her friends and the churchpeople who sent her gifts of money and clothing formed a simple and revealing diary of her struggles. On July 5, 1956, she wrote:

"The task of teaching and training so many is almost overwhelming; there are so many new ones coming in at all ages, none of them ever having been in school before; we have to start from the very bottom. We found that it was not good to put a new girl, eleven or twelve years old, with our babies who are just learning their ABC's. So we have made a special class for the new girls and boys. Some are quite bright and anxious to learn, and are soon able to rush ahead and catch up with several classes higher. But . . . some children are very dull and not able to keep up with the classes. Yet the rule of the Egyptian schools is that for the first three years all of the class must be promoted without an examination. Then at the end of the fourth year they are required to take a hard Government examination. Many of the children should never have passed some of the first grades, so by the time they have reached the fourth year, they are not at all prepared for a hard examination. This means that such backward children need private teaching if they are to pass. And with two hundred babies to take care of and all the sewing and cleaning and care of the sick, we just don't have enough big girls to do all of this. You have no idea of the amount of care and time that must be spent in keeping two hundred little tots and babies well and happy. And just when we get some of our best girls well trained, they get married and leave us. . . .

"Can you imagine what a great job it is to teach the Gospel to hundreds of children who come to us knowing nothing at all about it, to teach them so they will understand our standards of right and wrong and the principles on which our Christian faith is built and founded? It is indeed a great job for one must see that the child is educated in everything—not just one thing . . . and understand what we taught them well enough to pass it on. . . . I am trying to do my very best so that every day that passes may be a stepping stone, one step higher in some little orphan's life."

Mama wrote on August 14, 1956: "We are very short of missionaries. . . . Just now only Miss Mabel Dean and myself. Miss Shirley Newton, who has been helping me while the Reverend and Mrs. Philip Crouch are in America, was not able to renew her visa again, so she had to leave us. She did good work . . . taught a large number of the children typing, as well as her preaching and teaching. There was much she could have helped me do had she been allowed to remain in Egypt. There was just nothing we could do about it. The Reverend and Mrs. Joseph Brown have just arrived in America where they will be having a well-deserved rest. We have just heard that Mrs. Philip Crouch has decided not to return to Egypt at this time with their children . . . they have been with me in the Orphanage since 1948. They were in Egypt many years before that.

"As we are very much in need of a head for the very important post in Port Said, the Reverend George Carmichael has asked Brother Philip Crouch to take over the Bible school. [He] . . . has always been much interested in the spiritual training of young boys, so he has agreed to take over the Bible school for a year when he returns to Egypt in September."

On September 11, 1956, Mama wrote: "We are doing a lot of very important building, just now. I brought a large electric (dynamo) . . . engine from America. This we have just installed in a special new building and we had to have a new water engine and large reservoir and all of this is now being erected.

"Last year part of one of our old buildings fell down, so we are now rebuilding this also. We have been building ever since I returned from America [in 1955]. I was able to pay for all of these wonderful buildings . . . [with] the money given to me in the different churches where I spoke last year while I was in America, and money given from the showing of the film, "Nile Mother." I knew of our many needs here so I saved every cent above my absolute needs for food and travel." Once, Springfield, Missouri, friends reserved for Mama a hotel room at the convention where they had asked her to speak. The room was lovely and was to cost them nine dollars a day. When she arrived and discovered the price, she moved out immediately. Her babies needed that money for water machinery, she insisted. (It was given to her.) "All of these wonderful improvements will mean so much to us in years to come. . . . Our needs are fresh every day and I thank you for standing by me. I never forget that it is you in America and friends in Egypt who have enabled me to continue all of these years to keep our door wide open. . . ."

On October 1, 1956, Mama wrote: "Many of our friends are wondering how things are with us now that there is the trouble of the Suez Canal. We are very thankful indeed that nothing at all is changed with us in any way. No trouble in our school, church, or teaching. We feel that things will soon be peacefully settled. The Egyptians have always been very kind and helpful to us, for which we thank God. I know in whom I have believed and am persuaded that He is able to keep that which I have committed unto Him against that day."

Mama continued: "Last week a visitor, hearing that we had just opened a new school for the older boys (who were too many) said to me: 'But that will cost you an awful lot of money to run such a large school! Books, teachers. . . . How much will it cost you?' I said, 'Why, I don't know. But there are over a hundred boys and we must have the school.' He said, 'But do you mean to say you have already started the school and have not counted the cost of running it?' 'Why, yes,' I said, 'we never count the cost; we only look for the need. Then we go ahead and do it. God meets the needs as we go along. . . . Counting the cost way just isn't the way we run this Orphanage. It just has to be God!'

"We very seldom get a big donation," she wrote. "From five to ten dollars accounts for by far the greater part of our gifts. . . ." Then she added hopefully: "Don't wait until you are able to send a large sum. We have many needs which only cost a dollar! Perhaps your dollar would just fit in beautifully! (Most dollars do, you know!)"

Mama wrote on November 10, 1956: "We were indeed very sad to bid Miss Christie and Miss Burt goodbye as they left for America. . . . They have done a very good work here. . . . Today we were delighted to get our first American mail since the war started. . . .

"While writing, one of my girls came in telling me that her brother's wife gave birth to twins yesterday and died at once. The little girl is going now to the funeral and bring me the babies—if they are still alive.

"We are so thankful that we got our many new buildings finished as I expect it will be almost impossible to get permission to do any new building until Port Said has been rebuilt. . . . As far as we know, all of our missions are all right, but we do not know about the Bible school in Port Said. We have not heard from the pastor (the Reverend Ayad Chenuda), but I did get a letter from them just before the battle of Port Said.

"Another new child has just come in as I write—a poor little half-wit. He is also a cripple. Both his mother and father are dead. . . . Please pray for peace in beautiful Egypt."

On February 2, 1957, Mama wrote to America: "New children are coming in faster than ever before. It seems the war has made it very hard for the poor all over the country, and poor relatives feel that they can no longer support orphans. . . . Last month we took in twenty-eight new children! . . . I have just bought over a ton of cotton to make mattresses. We have enough blankets. I bought one thousand all-wool army blankets from money I was given in America. The W.M.C. ladies and friends sent me a lovely lot of sheets. The trouble is, where can we put the beds?"

In the last week of December, 1957, a near tragedy descended around Mama, in the form of polio. It was a frightening time which struck in the midst of joyous unpacking of gifts from America. In the rush of activity and the anxiety for her children, it was March, 1958, before Mama could speak of it in her newsletter to American friends. Finally, she was able to get her thoughts recorded: "I wonder if you can imagine how I felt one day during the last week in December when I found two babies in our infants' nursery with polio! I rushed them to the American hospital and the doctors there confirmed my fears! Then on New Year's Eve while unpacking all of the boxes of gifts from America two more were stricken with polio! My babies! Oh, just imagine hundreds of lovely little children! There was nothing I could do but look to God. All day I kept repeating that verse in the Ninety-first Psalm, verse 10—'Neither shall any plague come nigh thy dwelling.' We thank God that it is now about the middle of March and no new cases. Two of the children have returned from the hospital. The other was a very weak little baby whose mother died with tuberculosis. She got well from the polio, but she never got her strength back. She died last week.

"I wrote to Cairo trying to get some injections but was not able to get even one. Then, one morning I received a long-distance call from Cairo, from Mr. Picton of CARE, asking me if I could use some polio injections! I asked him how he had heard of our need. He had not heard about it at all. He sent a young man especially from Cairo with enough injections for two hundred twenty-five children. He brought them all packed in dry ice. Never before have I ever been offered any polio injections.

"You will be very pleased to hear that Pastor Ayad, of the Port Said Bible School, who was reported dead, is quite safe, and only minor damage was done to the Bible school building."

One of Mama's greatest personal tragedies took place in February, 1959, when she lost little Caroline. The beautiful little Egyptian girl was one of Mama's dearest companions.

Though Mama was seventy and the little girl only seven, the two were inseparable. Their closeness was accentuated by their great common bond: their love of babies. How a child of seven could be so mature in her love for Mama and the babies of the orphanage Mama could never understand. But that was how it was with Caroline. Gradually, it came to be understood that as Mama grew older Caroline would take over the babies. Already, in 1959, she could do innumerable tasks to help, and she loved doing those tasks. And she loved the babies. Tragedy in the form of leukemia took Caroline, leaving Mama sobbing quietly: "Who will take my place with my babies now? Who, with no Caroline?"

The little girl's life-sized picture hangs in the main lobby of the nursery today, looking alert and quizzical, seeming to ask the same question.

One of Mama's greatest pleasures through the years has been her close association with her older girls who make her a confidante in all their dreams and plans. Mama has an abundance of compassion for them, an overwhelming interest in them. And they know it. They tell her their problems and discuss them with her, sometimes for five minutes, sometimes off and on for weeks. Whatever time it takes for this, Mama takes it. If she doesn't have the time, somehow she makes it, then gives it. When she has corrected someone she always tries to explain why. Particularly in dealing with her teen-agers she tries to give her reason why she says 'no.' She believes firmly in good discipline. But when she is shown that she has punished someone unjustly, she always calls that one to her and apologizes.

Mama is proud of her grown children. Wherever she

goes in Egypt she finds them: William, son of a blind man, now founder of an excellent school in the Sudan; Philip, a professor in a government high school in Alexandria; Zacher, who has received his B.A. from the Faculty of Arts in Cairo, and stood fourth in his class; Edward, now working in an airplane factory; Robert, William's brother, a fine cabinetmaker; Eskander, a representative of a drug company. His appointment as representative was made directly from London, England. Askery is a clerk in a lawyer's office in Cairo. Shokery is a clerk in the English army, somewhere near Cairo; Gergus is in the Egyptian State Railway; Wadeah (a girl) works in the main office of the telephone exchange.

The remarkable list is endless. It could run into thousands of names. Seeing them as Christians and founding Christian homes in their own right gives Mama unspeakable joy. It is worth all it has cost her, she reminds herself often. Now, one of her boys grown to manhood, Mena Girgis, handles the accounting (which has been kept accurately since the orphanage first began and has been commended by Egyptian inspection officials who have come to go over her books—then have sent back their own offerings to help, sometimes as much as a hundred dollars). Mena also takes much of the administrative load of the orphanage from Mama's shoulders now and is invaluable to her in numerous ways.

Once Mama went to Cairo to speak at the YMCA there and went to see Faheema—one of her first girls, who had married a customs official. It turned into a family party with the house filled with her children and "grandchildren" who had come to honor her. She never could have counted the number of little boys named Trasher or the number of little girls name Lillian.

The mission house to which Mama came as a girl still remains, but the missionaries have long since gone. Only a few Egyptians go there for simple services on Sundays. But the old, nearly deserted mission stands as a perpetual shrine to Mama since it brought her to Egypt where she belonged.

The writing and sketching Mama longed to do as a girl have found an outlet in Egypt too. Before she had been there many years a book of her fables and sketches had been published. Many of the stories are the ones Mama has told her children through the years.

Recently a young American woman who had spent most of her life with her Presbyterian missionary parents in Africa decided to go to Egypt—as Mama's helper. How grateful Mama was to get her! Miss Ruth Anderson knew Arabic, knew and loved the Egyptian people and particularly Mama's children. And now that Mama was past seventy, the younger woman could help her immeasurably. Another young woman, Miss Rose Armenia, also came to help her, and Mama was grateful for the additional help. Previously, she had had a number of excellent workers and teachers, but now that she was old she needed help even more. However, the ever-prevalent money problem cropped up again. As of July, 1959, Mama had no means to pay this second helper a salary.

But this, too, had an answer, Mama knew. For that answer she knelt nightly in prayer. She wrote a newsletter to her good friends in America telling of the problem: "She [Rose] came before her support was promised," she wrote. Realizing that the churches were not aware of the situation, she continued: "I feel quite sure this is only because most people thought that she had her support before she came out. . . . Her family is doing what . . . [it] can. Of course, we will never let her suffer, but she does not want to take from us if it is at all possible for her to get support from kind friends at home."

And, as the members of these churches had done many times in the past, they answered her prayers. These devout Christians have taken offerings many times to help Mama. Formed in 1914, four years after Mama first went to Egypt as a girl, the Assemblies of God is known for its mission work through the world, supporting seven hundred and eighty foreign missionaries in its own right.

Mama's July, 1959, newsletter to them continued: "We have just taken in a little girl five and a half years old. Her mother is dead and her father married again, the stepmother beat her. . . . Poor baby, she is here now where she will be able to forget. . . .

"A few days ago a poor widow arrived with three little boys. . . . Now another widow has come also . . . five children. . . . Two little boys now . . . their father is paralyzed, the mother has to go work to feed the father. There is no end. . . ."

August 10, 1959, she wrote: "It does not sound much to say, 'A new baby arrived today.' It only takes a line in my letter to you. But it means twenty years of hard work before we have a nice young man ready to go out and start on his own, or a nice young girl bids me 'Goodbye' with her pretty wedding veil blowing in the breeze as she leaves the only home she has known. But don't forget the years between. Sickness—all the children's diseases known. Schooling, clothing, feeding, correcting, prayers, tears. Oh, those long years full of all the joys and sorrows. . . ."

September 10, 1959: "Mr. Mena's oldest daughter was engaged last Saturday. It was indeed a joyful day. Mrs. Mena made a big feast for about three hundred of our little girls and boys. They killed a big calf and made a lovely stew and all came and sat in the garden. They had the largest pieces of meat they had ever had in their lives! The Egyptians feel that if they are made happy they should do something to make the less fortunate happy too. While they were enjoying the meal a very small little girl was sitting with her back to me. She turned, looked up in my face and said, 'Mama, do you know this is the blessing of the Lord?' I said, 'Yes, darling, it is indeed.' "

On December 10, 1959, Mama wrote in her newsletter to America: "I have just received a letter asking me to try to go to America for a Sunday School Convention which will be held in Minneapolis, Minnesota, May 3, 4, and 5. I have written and told them that, God willing, I will go, perhaps leaving Egypt sometime in the middle of March. I expect to spend the summer in America as the heat is too great for me to spend the whole summers in Assiout . . . I am really very much in need of a real change."

There are still great needs at the orphanage. With its English, leathercraft, machine, sewing classes, and regular school as well as the newer private day school for well-to-do Egyptian children, its increased numbers (1275), the orphanage is a mighty force and a mighty responsibility. Mama spent a total of $71,241.39 in 1958 not counting thousands of dollars' worth of foodstuffs sent her by the

American government and great supplies of clothing sent her by the women of the Assemblies of God. She received during that year $44,598.56 in foreign donations and $16,606.62 from Egyptian donations; $7,205.68 miscellaneously, and $953.85 by subscription in Egypt. Mama keeps none of the money for herself except when someone occasionally sends a check or money directed for her personal use only. The favorable rate of exchange from American money to Egyptian helps Mama immeasurably. American money simply goes further when changed to Egyptian money.

In spite of better circumstances Mama often has only enough to run her for two or three weeks. It is surprising how many little things she has needed but has managed to do without all these years. In July, 1959, she wrote to her friends in America that she badly needed some baby scales so she could weigh her youngest babies!

In the autumn of 1959, Mama's new car which had been sent her by a group of missionary-minded young people in the United States arrived at an Egyptian port, but was held for large (100%) customs fees. It would have been impossible for Mama to have raised the necessary amount. When the Egyptian government was informed of her plight, the new car was released to her without charges. Shortly thereafter she received a letter from the President of Egypt, Mr. Nasser, which read in part: "It gives me pleasure to learn that you got the car free of expense as you requested. I would like to tell you that your work for the orphans is very much appreciated by everyone in this country. . . . I wish you continued success in your philanthropic endeavour."

Mama was seventy-three in September, 1960. The year 1960 makes a half a century she has been in Egypt loving, feeding, housing, teaching her tremendous family by faith alone. This in a land of about twenty-five million Moslems.

During the half century about eight thousand have called her Mama in the big Assiout Orphanage. Not one of her children has brought her any disgrace in a half a century. Millions of Egyptians of all ranks love and respect her across this ancient land.

Go to any port or village or city in the nation and say the name "Mama Lillian," and somber eyes will light up and unsmiling lips will smile. Even if they have never seen her, Egyptians everywhere feel they *know* her.

Mama has come a long, long way since she knelt as a child beside a fallen log in Georgia and vowed: "Lord, if I can ever do anything to help You, just let me know and I'll do it!"